HOMEWORK HELPERS
Sticker Book

Contents

HOMEWORK HELPERS
Spelling

Written by Amanda Archer
Illustrated by Ian Cunliffe
Educational Consultant: Geraldine Taylor

The journey from A to Z

Every word is made up of letters from the **alphabet**.
The alphabet has 26 letters.

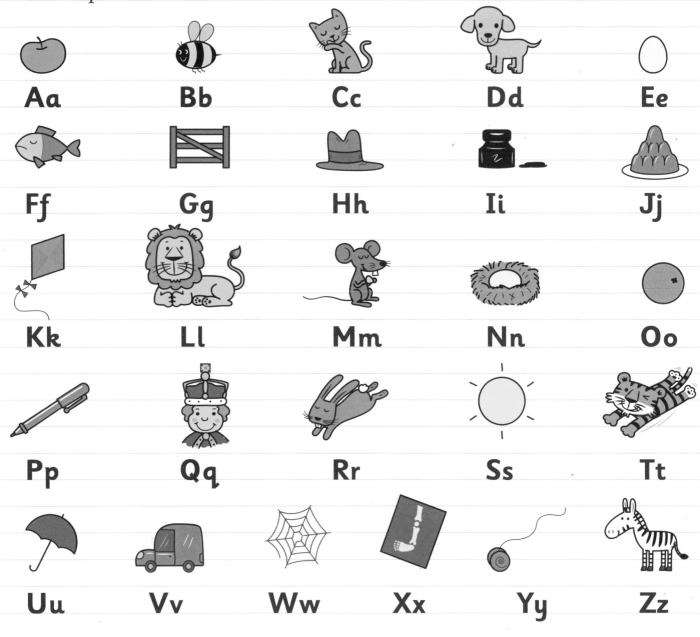

Aa	Bb	Cc	Dd	Ee
Ff	Gg	Hh	Ii	Jj
Kk	Ll	Mm	Nn	Oo
Pp	Qq	Rr	Ss	Tt
Uu	Vv	Ww	Xx	Yy
				Zz

Let's get started!

Find the missing letter stickers to start these words.

( ) ap   ( ) rum   ( ) lock   ( ) pider

Happy endings

Finish the words in this beach scene by writing in the last letters.

1.boa_

2.umbrell_

4.shel_

3.cra_

5.octopu_

Sticker star time!

6.starfis_

Letter types

Five letters of the alphabet are called **vowels**.

Aa

Ii

Ee

Oo

Uu

The rest are called **consonants**.

There are 21 **consonants** in the alphabet.

Jungle japes
Stick the missing letters onto this curly alphabet snake.

a b c d e f h i j k m

Short and sweet

Short vowel sounds don't take long to say!

Write **a** or **e** to complete these words.

c_t   b_d

Write **i** or **o** to complete these words.

p_n   f_x

Write **u** or **e** to complete these words.

s_n   p_g

These words all have short vowel sounds.

A little longer

These words have **long** vowel sounds – can you
hear the difference between short and long vowels?

Add the right vowel to complete these words.

 b_e

k_te

fl_te

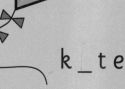

Sticker
star
time!

7

Lots of plurals

A **plural** means 'more than one thing'. We make most nouns plural by adding **s** to the end of the word. Add a sticker to make each word more than one.

apple ⬚   cup ⬚

A **noun** is another way of describing a naming word.

When a noun ends in **s, x, sh** or **ch** we make it plural by adding **es** to the end. Add a sticker to make each word plural.

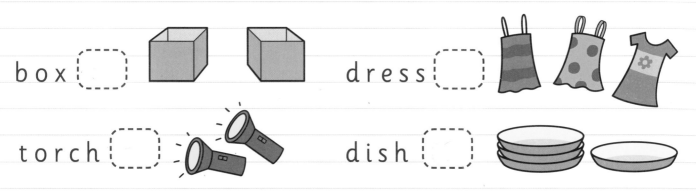

box ⬚   dress ⬚

torch ⬚   dish ⬚

Sometimes, when a noun ends in a consonant followed by the letter **y**, such as 'lady', we take off the **y** and add the letters **ies**. Add a picture for each of these words.

one lorry   one baby

two lorries   two babies

Farm count-up

This farm is full of examples of plurals. Some follow rules and some don't. Work out the correct plurals and add word stickers to describe each set of animals.

Sticker star time!

Delightful describing

Adjectives are describing words, such as **big** and **friendly**.
Some adjectives can be made by adding **y** to a noun.

Add a word sticker to describe each picture below.

To make the words below into adjectives you **double the last letter and then add y**. Look at the first one, then change the other words to adjectives. Find a picture sticker for each word.

sun**ny**   mud__   spot__

If a noun ends with **e, take off the e and add y** to make an adjective.
Write in the adjectives below. The first one has been done for you.

wave	stone	slime	rose
wav**y**	_ _ _ _ _	_ _ _ _ _	_ _ _ _

stripe	nose	ice	shine
_ _ _ _ _ _	_ _ _ _	_ _ _	_ _ _ _ _

10

Weather watch

It's been a wacky week for weather!

Can you fill in the weather chart with the missing word stickers?

Adjectives tell you more about nouns. They make your sentences more interesting to read.

Monday	
Tuesday	
Wednesday	
Thursday	
Friday	
Saturday	
Sunday	

Sticker star time!

Weighing up words

We can add **er** or **est** to the end of many adjectives when we want to compare things:

My scarf is long, Zara's is long**er**, but Felix has the long**est** of all.

Add the missing picture sticker to finish comparing the words.

f a s t   f a s t **e r**   f a s t **e s t**

If the adjective ends in the letter **y**, change the **y** to an **i** before adding **er** or **est**:

I am happy, but Ava is happ**ier** and Jacob is happ**iest** of all.

Add the missing picture sticker below.

f u n n y   f u n n **i e r**   f u n n **i e s t**

Use **er** when you are comparing two things. Use the **est** ending when you are comparing more than two things.

Park puzzle

The footballers are having fun in the park! Add the stickers to complete these sets of comparing words.

tall

tall**est**

high**er**

high

dirty

dirt**ier**

small

smallest

Sticker star time!

Right here, right now

We add **ing** to the end of verbs to show that something is happening now. Add a sticker to describe what each child is doing.

When a word has a **short** vowel sound (such as the sound **o** in hop) we **double the last letter before we add ing**.

Spell the **ing** words below. The first one has been done for you.

hop**ping**   sit_____   dig_____

When the word ends in **e**, we **take off the e before we add ing**. Write the new words here. The first one has been done for you.

ride + ing = riding   care + ing = _____

move + ing = _____   make + ing = _____

A trip to the circus

Write the missing action word next to each happy character.

An action or doing word is called a **verb**. When we write about things that are happening now, we are using the **present tense** of the verb.

The girl is c_____ her hands.

The strongman is l_____ weights.

This clown is r_____ on his unicycle.

This clown is j_____ balls.

15

Done and dusted

We add **ed** to the end of verbs to show that something
has already happened.
Write the past tense of the verbs below.

push + ed = _ _ _ _ _ _   pull + ed = _ _ _ _ _ _

When the word has a short vowel sound (such as the **u** in rub) we
double the last letter and add **ed**.
Write the endings to these verbs. The first has been done for you.

clapped   jog_ _ _   hop_ _ _

When the word ends in **e**, we **take off the e before we add ed**.
Write the new words here. The first one has been done for you.

like + ed = liked   race + ed = _ _ _ _ _

smile + ed = _ _ _ _ _ _   hope + ed = _ _ _ _ _

It's only got one **boot**.

His pupils were too **bright**.

Because it saw the tree **bark**.

A woolly **jumper**.

page 6–7

l

q

g

w

children

sheep

horses

page 9

mice

fish

cows

witch

knife

page 22

whale

wreck

smell**y**

page 10

hair**y**

dirt**y**

page 20

page 25

stairs

room

stairs

room

shine

paper

page 20

page 8

page 20

page 22

page 22

flour

page 20

page 20

blew

page 10

page 20

page 28

page 20

leek

page 10

page 20

sun

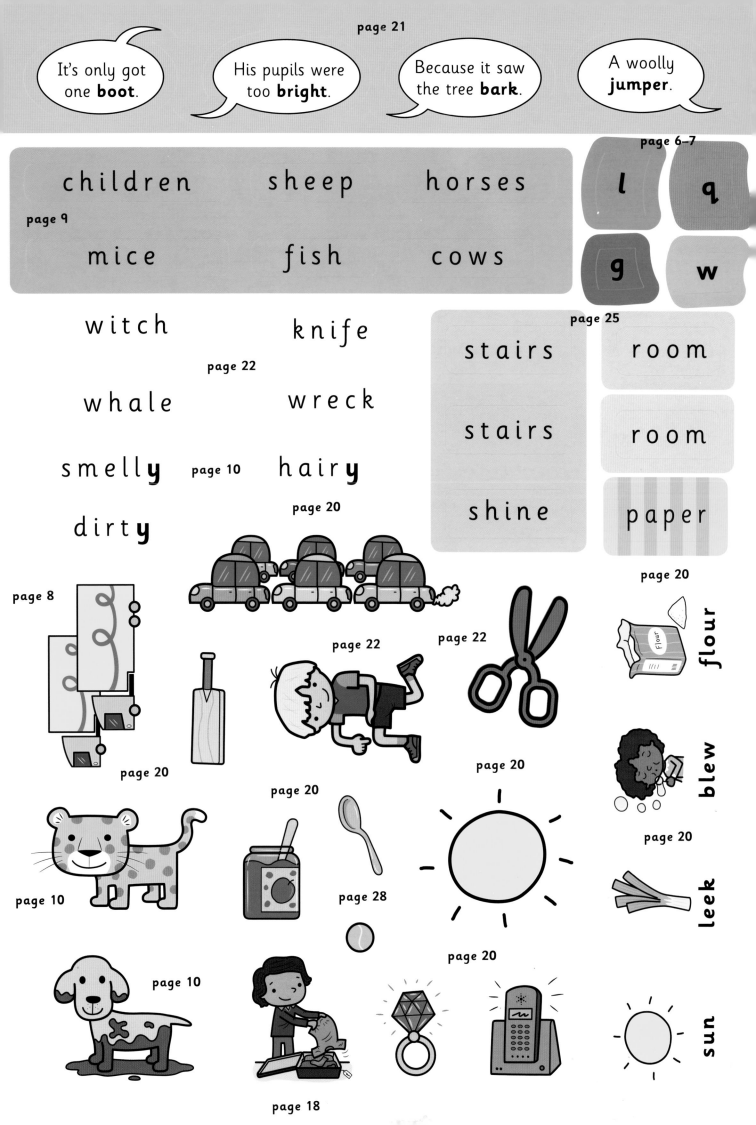

page 18

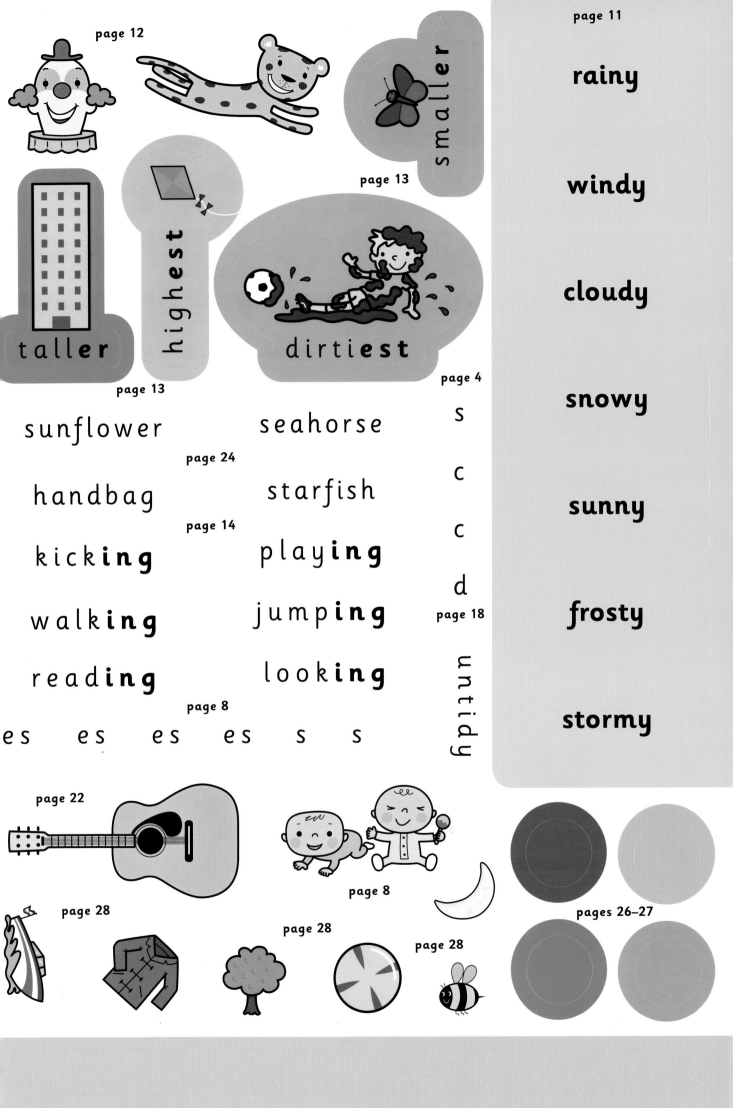

page 11

rainy

windy

cloudy

snowy

sunny

frosty

stormy

page 12

page 13

smaller

highest

tall**er**

dirti**est**

page 13

sunflower

seahorse

page 24

handbag

starfish

page 14

kick**ing**

play**ing**

walk**ing**

jump**ing**

read**ing**

look**ing**

page 8

es   es   es   es   s   s

page 4

s

c

c

d

page 18

untidy

page 22

page 28

page 28

page 8

page 28

pages 26–27

Rowdy rulebreakers!

Some verbs change one letter or more when things have already happened.

For example, r**u**n becomes r**a**n.

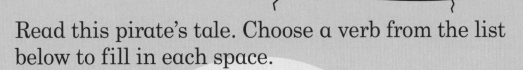

When we write about things that have already happened, we are using the **past tense** of a verb.

Read this pirate's tale. Choose a verb from the list below to fill in each space.

Greetings, me hearties!

One sunset I _ _ _ another ship pass in the distance. I gave the order to raise the mainsail. The wind _ _ _ _ us there in no time. As soon as we got close by, my men _ _ _ to grab their weapons. They could tell that the ship belonged to pirates, like us!

I _ _ _ downstairs in my cabin, trying to come up with a plan. Just then there was a knock on the door. My cabin boy explained that the strange ship belonged to my brother, Old Jack Barnacles!

That night we _ _ _ a grand feast, both crews singing until the early hours.

The funniest thing about our jolly evening? My lazy parrot, George, _ _ _ _ _ _ through the whole party!

One-Eyed Toby

saw	blew	ran	sat	ate	slept

Sticker star time!

What is the opposite?

We can add **un** to the beginning of some words to make them mean the opposite:

kind   unkind

Find a picture or word sticker to show the opposites below.

h a p p y   u n h a p p y   p a c k   u n p a c k

t i d y   [   ]

Adding **dis** at the front of other words can turn them into opposites too.

like   dislike

Write in the words to finish off the **dis** word sums below.

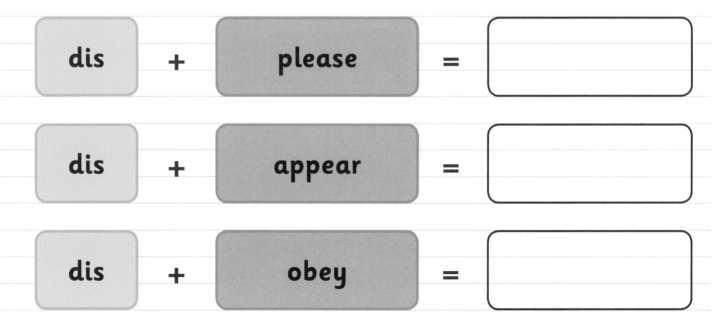

dis	+	please	=	
dis	+	appear	=	
dis	+	obey	=	

All change!
Complete the sentences.

It was time for the children to get __dressed, ready for PE.

Gemma __tied her shoelaces and pulled off her hat.

Sarah __zipped her jacket and hung it on a hook.

Thomas ___liked the green T-shirt he had to wear.

There aren't any rules for choosing when to add **un** or **dis**. You need to learn the words off by heart.

Sticker star time!

The same but different

Some words sound the same, but have a different spelling and meaning. These words are called **homophones**.

Picture pairs
Look at the words below, then add the picture stickers to sort them into pairs.

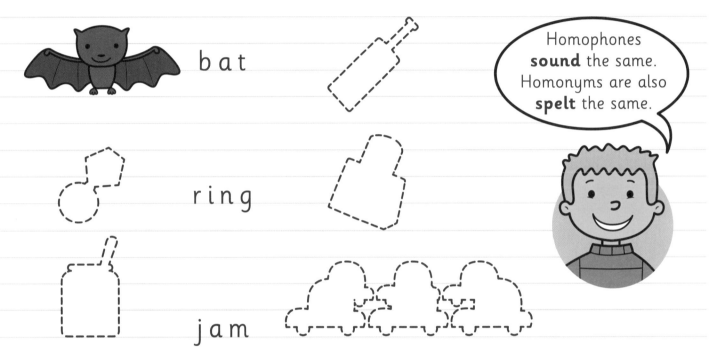

b a t

r i n g

j a m

Homophones **sound** the same. Homonyms are also **spelt** the same.

Sounds like...
Add the picture stickers to sort these homophones into pairs.

hair   hare

pair   pear

flower

blue

son

leak

Homonyms are words that sound the same and are spelt the same, but have different meanings.

Jolly jokes

A great way to learn about homonyms is to swap jokes with your friends. Stick the right funny answers to the jokes below.

What sort of dancing do plumbers like?

Tap dancing!

Why can't a car play football?

Why did the teacher wear sunglasses?

Why did the cat jump out of the tree?

What do you get if you cross a sheep with a kangaroo?

Sticker star time!

21

Shh! Letters in hiding

Some words contain letters that you can't hear when you say them out loud – for example, you can't hear the **w** in wrong.

Say the words and find the correct sticker.

These letters are known as **silent letters**.

Find the picture stickers for the words below. Do you know which letters are silent?

guitar   knee   scissors

Funny photos!

This photo album is packed with silent letters. Write in the missing words.

The happy family group. That's me kneeling on the floor.

A sweet little _ _ _ _ .

Daisy _ _ _ _ _ _ _ _ along the beach.

Maria _ _ _ _ _ _ _ to her friend.

Grandad's new garden _ _ _ _ _ .

Sticker star time!

Two for the price of one

Some words can be joined with others to create a brand-new word.

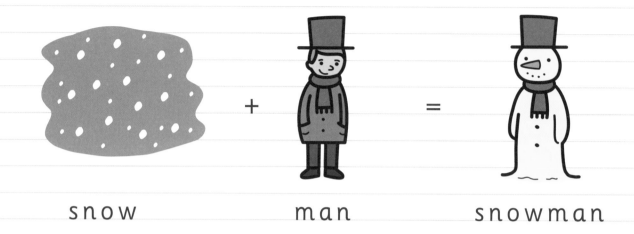

snow   +   man   =   snowman

Say the new word and add in the word sticker.

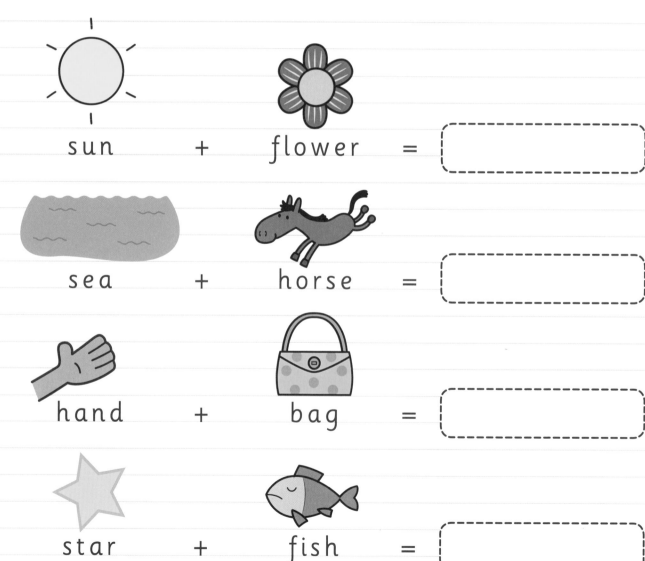

sun   +   flower   =

sea   +   horse   =

hand   +   bag   =

star   +   fish   =

24

Find the compounds

Find the correct word stickers to finish off the labels on this house.

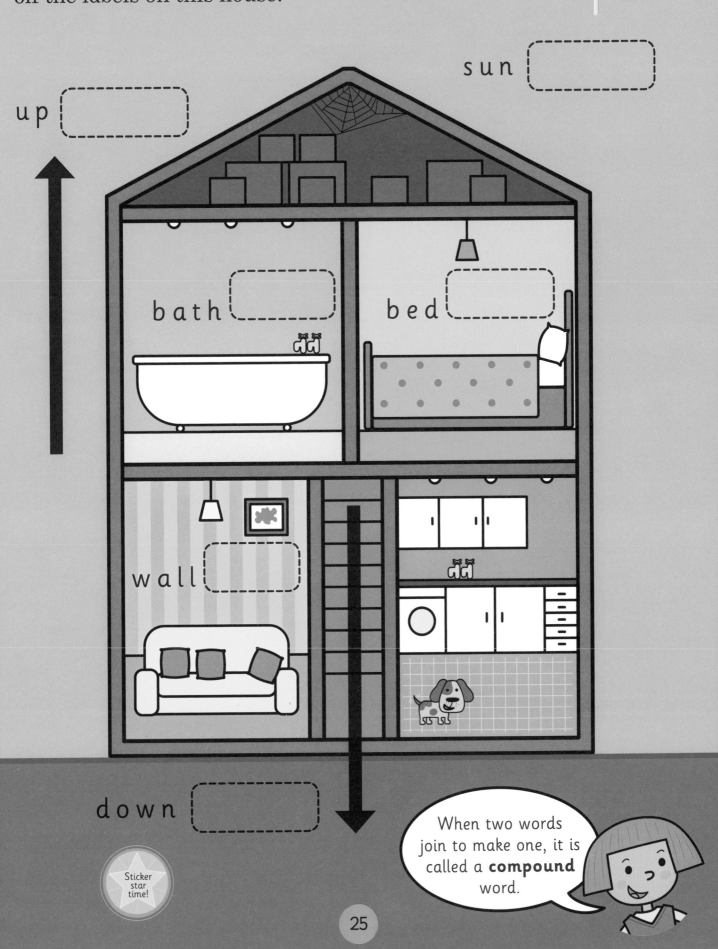

up

sun

bath

bed

wall

down

When two words join to make one, it is called a **compound** word.

The great zoo race

START – say three words beginning with 'a'.

Go straight to the flamingos.

3

Name all t[he] vowels.

Play this game with up to three friends. Press the coloured stickers onto card and carefully cut them out. Choose a coloured counter each.

Hear the lions roar. Take an extra throw.

14

13

16

The tigers wake up. Move forward two spaces.

18

How to play

Take turns to throw a die, then move across the board as fast as you can. Follow the instructions on each square.

Each red square has a special challenge. If the others agree that it has been completed successfully, the player may move forward one extra square.

Good luck!

29

The penguins are all in the water. Go back two spaces.

27

30

What is a noun?

32

Think of four adjectives.

42

Use **er** and **est** to compare th[e] size of you[r] fingers.

Lose your map. Go back to square 30.

45

Say three words starti[ng] with **un** or **dis**.

t lost on the way to the nguins. Miss a turn.	**6**	Name the 12th letter of the alphabet.	Say two words that end with 'd'.
ut out seven onsonants.	**11**	Stop at the café. Miss a turn.	**9**
Say a letter at completes hese words: _p, h_g, p_t.	Take the zoo train to square 25.	**21**	Say three words with a long 'oo' sound in the middle.
he reptile use is too usy. Miss a turn.	**25**	The giant spider doesn't scare you. Skip to square 30.	The polar bears are playing. Miss a turn.
What is the plural of 'tooth'?	**34**	It's feeding time! Go directly to square 38.	**36**
40	Tell a short story in the past tense.	**38**	**37**
Say two omophones.	Take photos of the zebras. Miss a turn.	Shout out five compound words.	FINISH

Super word quiz

Rhyme time
Add a picture sticker to each word. Then, say the words and listen for the vowel sounds. Next, draw lines to match the words that rhyme.

boat   bee

tree   spoon

moon   coat

Compare the creatures
Look at the animals in each box, then circle the smallest butterfly, the biggest elephant, the hairiest bear and the stripiest tiger.

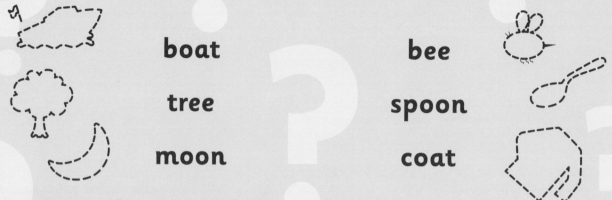

Keep your eye on the ball
There is a ball missing from each picture. Add the ball stickers, then write in the missing action word.

_ _ _ _

_ _ _

Homophone fill-in

Look at the homophones at the top of each box.
Read the words then write them in the sentence.

blew   blue

She _____ up the _____ balloon.

I   eye

_ have a sore ___.

sea   see

He can ___ the ___.

Land ahoy!

Can you complete this spelling scene? Choose from the word list below and write the correct one above each picture.

island
waves
ship
hat
pirate
tree

Tricky words

Some words are quite difficult to spell and you need to learn and remember them.

Have a look at the word lists below. Cover them up and try to write them down without looking again. Put a tick next to the ones you get right.

said _____ ☐

children _____ ☐

about _____ ☐

people _____ ☐

house _____ ☐

asked _____ ☐

could _____ ☐

water _____ ☐

where _____ ☐

school _____ ☐

Look, say, cover, write, check

Here are some more tricky words for you to practise. Remember to **look** first, **say** the word, then **cover** it up while you write it out. **Check** to see if you were correct.

know	_____	☐
round	_____	☐
thought	_____	☐
animals	_____	☐
through	_____	☐
found	_____	☐
around	_____	☐
laughed	_____	☐
different	_____	☐
suddenly	_____	☐

Sticker star time!

Reward chart

Use this chart to keep a record of your progress.

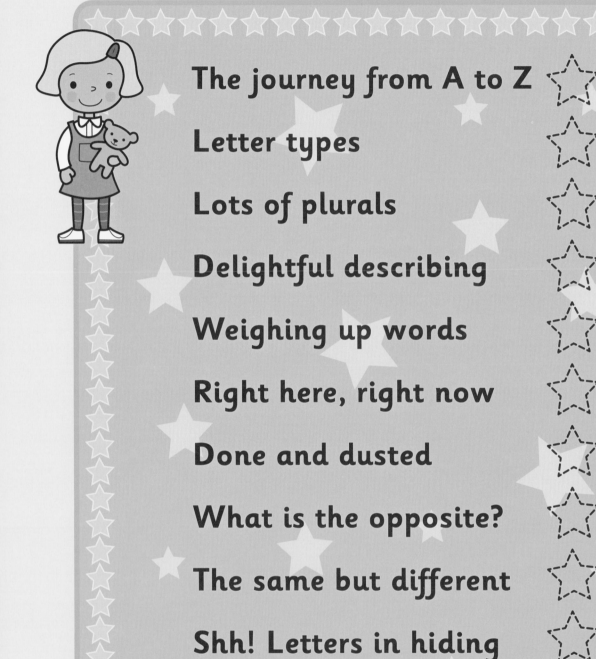

The journey from A to Z

Letter types

Lots of plurals

Delightful describing

Weighing up words

Right here, right now

Done and dusted

What is the opposite?

The same but different

Shh! Letters in hiding

Two for the price of one

Tricky words

HOMEWORK HELPERS

Grammar and Punctuation

Written by Emily Guille-Marrett

Illustrated by Ian Cunliffe

Nouns

Common nouns are the names given to general things or people.

tree

chair

mouse

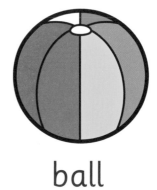

ball

man

woman

A noun is a word used to name things.

Proper nouns are the names given to people, places and official titles. Proper nouns always start with a capital letter.

Ben

Anjani

Marco

Rachel

Jamaica

New York

Queen Victoria

Eiffel Tower

Nouns – continued

Collective nouns are the names given to groups of things.

team

flock

litter

herd

swarm

bouquet

A noun is a word used to name things.

Abstract nouns are the names given to feelings or thoughts.

anger

love

hope

courage

joy

wisdom

Singular and plural

Plurals usually end in the letter **s** but some do not and we call these irregular.

Singular (one thing)   **Plural** (two or more)

cat		cats	
book		books	
car		cars	
skirt		skirts	
dish		dishes	
baby		babies	
child		children	
knife		knives	

**Singular means just one thing.
Plural means more than one thing.**

Some nouns have just one word for both singular and plural. They cannot be counted like ordinary nouns.

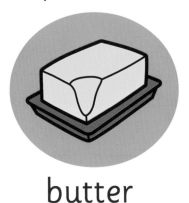

butter

sand

water

money

flour

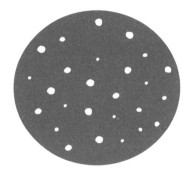

snow

Pronouns

Here are two ways of writing the same thing.

1. Millie likes to dance. **Millie** dances every day.

2. Millie likes to dance. **She** dances every day.

The second example uses the personal pronoun **she** to avoid repeating the proper noun **Millie**. This makes the sentences read in a smoother way.

A pronoun is often used to take the place of a noun in a sentence to avoid repeating it.

There are a number of different ways to use a **pronoun**.

1. Here are some examples of **personal pronouns** replacing nouns.

He plays rugby.

They like eating oranges.

The baby rattled **it**.

Grandma made **us** a cake.

2. **Possessive pronouns** show that something belongs to someone. Here are some examples.

The computer is **mine**.

The games are **yours**.

The toys are **ours**.

The book is **his** not **hers**.

Adjectives

Adjectives have been used to describe the noun **dog** in the pictures below.

thin dog

fat dog

white dog

brown dog

muddy dog

spotty dog

An adjective gives us information about a noun or a pronoun.

big dog

small dog

fast dog

wet dog

hairy dog

greedy dog

Adjectives – continued

Adjectives can be used to compare two or more things or people.

small   smaller   smallest

fast   faster   fastest

muddy   muddier   muddiest

An adjective gives us information about a noun or a pronoun.

Using adjectives can make your writing more interesting. Try using different adjectives when you write.

big
colossal, enormous, gigantic, huge, large, massive, mighty

cross
angry, annoyed, frustrated, fuming, irate, miffed

happy
content, delighted, ecstatic, enchanted, merry, overjoyed

pretty
beautiful, handsome, lovely, picturesque, radiant, stunning

If you find yourself using the same word and you can't think of something else, use a book called a **thesaurus** to help you find different words.

Verbs

walk

run

eat

drink

play

ride

A verb tells us what is happening in a sentence. It is a 'doing' word.

jump

hop

wait

read

swim

sleep

Verb tenses

Verbs can tell us when something happens.

1. Verbs in the present tense tell us that something is happening now.

   I paint a picture.

   I am painting a picture.

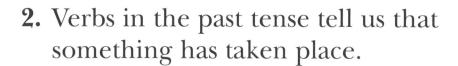

2. Verbs in the past tense tell us that something has taken place.

   I painted a picture.

   I was painting a picture.

3. Verbs in the future tense tell us that something is going to happen. The word **will** is often used to show the future.

   I will paint a picture tomorrow.

Irregular verbs

Most verbs in the past tense end in the letters **ed**.

However, some verbs do not follow this pattern and they are called **irregular verbs**.
Here are some irregular verbs:

Present tense	Past tense
I am	I was
I catch	I caught
I eat	I ate
I get	I got
I make	I made
I run	I ran
I see	I saw
I swim	I swam

Adverbs

1. Some **adverbs** tell us **how** something happens. They usually end in the letters **ly**.

He ran home **quickly**.

I shouted **loudly**.

She played the piano **beautifully**.

An adverb adds to the meaning of a verb or gives the sentence additional information.

2. Some **adverbs** tell us **when** something happens.

I have a ballet class **now**.

The bus will be here **soon**.

We have maths **after** break.

Adverbs – continued

3. Some **adverbs** tell us **where** something happens.

It was too wet to play **outside**.

The rabbit hopped **away**.

I ran **home**.

An adverb adds to the meaning of a verb or gives the sentence additional information.

4. Some **adverbs** tell us by **how much** something happens.

The tortoise is **really** slow.

We **almost** missed the train.

It was **too** cold to eat ice cream.

5. Some adverbs tell us **how often** something happens.

I brush my teeth **regularly**.

My friend **never** lies.

We **always** eat fruit.

Sentences

A written **sentence** always starts with a capital letter and usually ends with a **full stop (.)** .

Charlie opened his birthday presents.

capital letter

full stop

A sentence ends in a full stop, question mark or an exclamation mark.

If a question is being asked, a sentence ends with a **question mark (?)** .

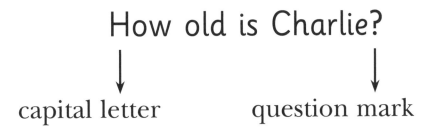

How old is Charlie?

capital letter   question mark

To express emotion, like surprise, some written sentences end with an **exclamation mark (!)** .

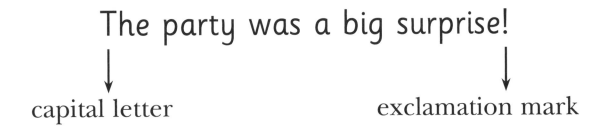

The party was a big surprise!

capital letter   exclamation mark

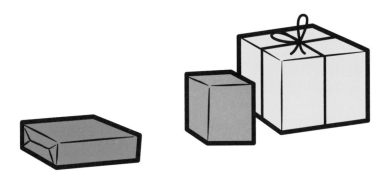

Commas

A **comma (,)** is used to help sentences make more sense by breaking them up into smaller portions.

Although it was sunny, it felt cold outside.

Here are two more examples of how a comma can be used.

1. To separate items in a list.

I like to eat fish, rice, peas and beans.

2. To add extra information within a sentence.

Jane, my sister, is only two years old.

Speech marks

We use **speech marks (" ")** to show that someone is speaking. All the spoken words must go inside the speech marks.

A comma is used to separate the spoken words from the unspoken words.

"The glass slipper is mine," said Cinderella.
"It won't fit," said the ugly sisters.

A comma is not needed if the sentence ends in a question mark or an exclamation mark.

"Will you marry me?" asked the prince.
"Yes!" Cinderella replied.

Apostrophes – missing letters

1. The apostrophe can be used to show a missing letter or letters when words are shortened.

It's snowing. Let's make a snowman!

I have	I've
I am	I'm
it is	it's
I will	I'll
they have	they've
we are	we're
did not	didn't
could not	couldn't

Apostrophes – belonging to

2. The apostrophe followed by the letter **s** can also be used to show that something belongs to someone or something.

It is Fiona's tennis ball.

I want to play at Sam's house.

That is the cat's bowl.

What is today's date?

Remember the difference between **it's** and **its**!

It's means "it is" or "it has".

It's Friday today.

Its means "belonging to it".

The mouse ate its food.

Notes

HOMEWORK HELPERS
Adding Up

Written by Amanda Archer
Illustrated by Ian Cunliffe
Educational Consultant: Geraldine Taylor

Party puzzlers

All adding up starts with good counting skills.

Count the candles
How many candles can you count on these birthday cakes?
Write the number next to each one. This number is the **total**.

□ candles   □ candles   □ candles

Use the candle
stickers to decorate
this cake. How
many are there?
Write in the total.   □ candles

How many children
are at my party?
I've made an ice cream
for each one.

There are □
children at your
party.

62

Fun with one

Count the objects below, then add one more
to each from the sticker sheet.
Write the correct numbers in the boxes.

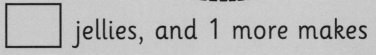 party hats, and 1 more makes ☐

 sandwiches, and 1 more makes ☐

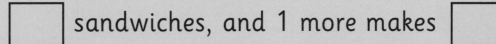 balls, and 1 more makes ☐

 jellies, and 1 more makes ☐

Sticker star time!

When you count
one more, you are
adding one.

Sums at the shops

Sometimes when we are counting on, we need to add **two more** things to the total.

Two for tea
The twins are coming for tea so you need to buy two more of everything.

Write the new totals below.

add 2 more to make ☐

add 2 more to make ☐

add 2 more to make ☐

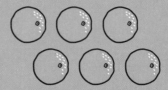

add 2 more to make ☐

Plus 2 practice
Look at each of the sums below then write in the correct answer.

2 + 7 = ☐   6 + 2 = ☐   8 + 2 = ☐

The word **equals** (or the symbol **=**), is another way of saying **makes**.

Sticker star time!

Some more sums

Can you work out the answers to these sums?
Put the correct answer stickers in place.

You can use the **+** symbol or the word **plus** to show that you are adding.

9 + 2 =

4 + 2 =

2 + 5 =

Zero zone

Now you can't carry another thing! What happens if you add zero more items to your shopping bags? Write in the answers.

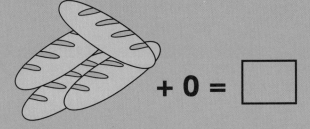 + 0 =

+ 0 =

Zero is another word for **none**.

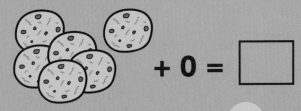 + 0 =

To ten and beyond

Ten pin teaser

There are lots of sums at the bowling alley.
Look at the questions below and write the answers in the boxes.

add = ☐

add = ☐

add = ☐

add = ☐

If I knock down 5 pins with my first throw, how many do I need to knock down with my next throw to score a perfect 10?

☐

Spot the spots

A game of dominoes can help us to practise adding up to 12. Count the spots on each section of the dominoes and write the numbers in the boxes.

Now stick in the correct total for each domino.

A **dozen** is another word for 12.

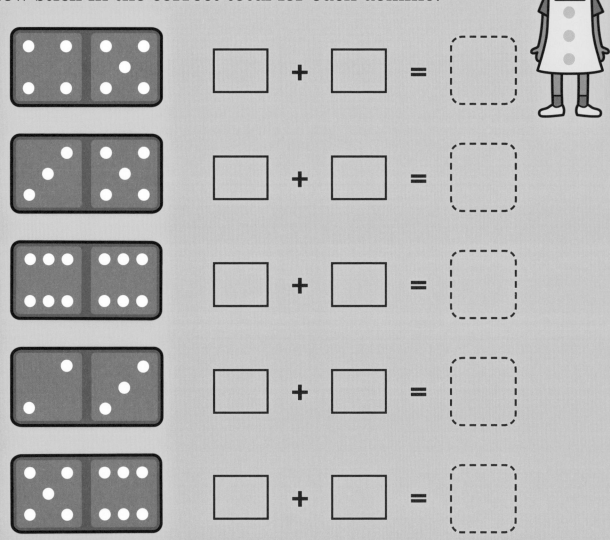

☐ + ☐ = ☐

☐ + ☐ = ☐

☐ + ☐ = ☐

☐ + ☐ = ☐

☐ + ☐ = ☐

Can you find two more picture stickers that feature the number 12?

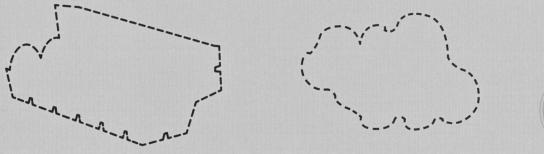

Sticker star time!

Maths chatter

There are many different words that tell us when it is time to use addition.

more

plus

altogether

and

add

total

sum

Animal antics

Write in the answers to the animal sums below.

 and more equals ☐

 add equals ☐

What is the sum of  and ☐

What is the total of  plus ☐

If  and live in your street, ☐
how many animals are there altogether?

All the right answers

Different combinations of numbers can add up to the same total.

Nibbling numbers

Look at the sums in the air bubbles, then stick in the right answer fish.

7 + 2

6 + 9

1 + 10

6 + 3

2 + 13

8 + 3

8 + 1

8 + 7

5 + 6

5 + 4

7 + 8

2 + 9

Sticker star time!

Up and down the line

A **number line** can help us with adding up.

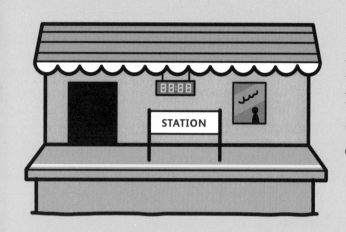

Put your finger on the bigger number in the sum and then count on the smaller number. When you finish counting, you have your answer.

Write the answers to the sums below in the boxes. Use the number line to help you if you need to.

16 + 5 = ☐   4 + 4 = ☐

8 + 8 = ☐   13 + 7 = ☐

14 + 5 = ☐

3 + 9 = ☐

| 1 | 2 | 3 | 4 | 5 | 6 | 7 | 8 | 9 | 10 | 11 |

A faster way of moving along the number line is to count in bigger steps, such as 2s and 5s.

Train-track maths

Now try these sums. Write the answers in the boxes. When you have finished, stick the train stickers next to the track.

9 + 4 = ☐   2 + 13 = ☐

10 + 8 = ☐   15 + 4 = ☐

| 12 | 13 | 14 | 15 | 16 | 17 | 18 | 19 | 20 | 21 | 22 |

Sticker
star
time!

Playing with numbers

Adding up can help us learn how numbers work.
A whole number like 10 is made up of parts.
If you know the parts you can put them together
again to make a whole.

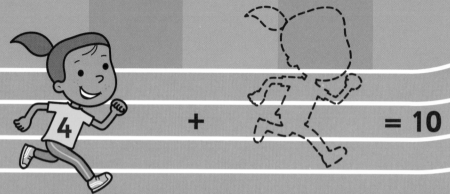

$4 + = 10$

Perfect pairs
Find a partner for
each child. Each number
pair must add up to 10.

$7 + = 10$

$6 + = 10$

All these perfect pairs
are called **number
pairs**. They all add up
to the same total.

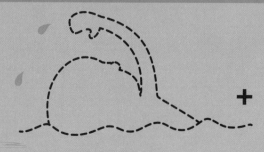 

$+ 5 = 10$

Super sets

Split this set of 20 footballs into two parts by drawing a circle around some of them. Now count up how many are in each section.

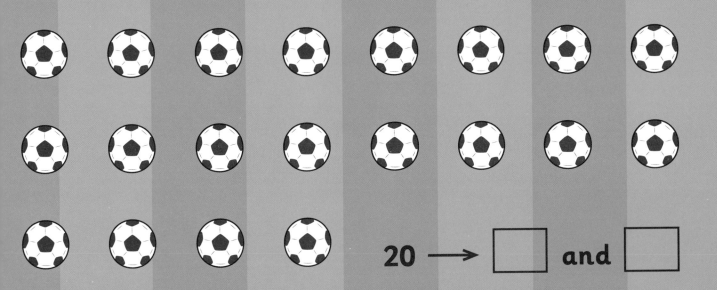

20 → ☐ and ☐

Now split this set of 12 tennis rackets into two parts by drawing a circle around some of them. How many are in each section?

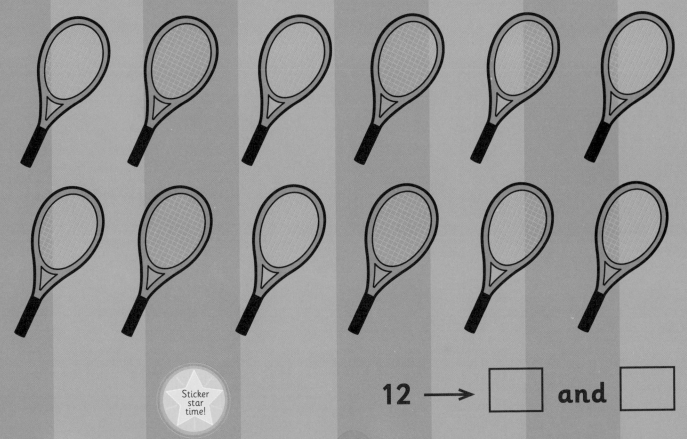

Sticker star time!

12 → ☐ and ☐

73

Swap shop

Now let's try adding three numbers together.

Top toys

Work out the answers to the sums below, then follow the lines to see if you are right.

20 + 7 + 3 =

6 + 3 + 3 =

2 + 3 + 4 =

30

12

9

Adding more and more

Jungle hide and seek
Can you see the creatures in the trees? Work out the sums to find out how many animals are hiding and write your answers in the boxes.

5 + 10 + 12 = ☐

7 + 7 + 7 + 8 = ☐

1 + 3 + 4 + 1 = ☐

9 + 11 + 3 = ☐

10 + 13 + 17 = ☐

3 + 4 + 2 + 6 = ☐

Sticker star time!

The sky's the limit!

Some addition problems have numbers missing. We need to use the numbers we have to work out what is missing.

Cloud cover

Fill in the blanks in these problems. Take the first number away from the answer to work out what the missing number is.

For example: $12 +$ ⬚ $= 35$

$(35 - 12 = 23$, so 23 is the number that goes in the box.)

When you finish each one, put the correct picture sticker in front of the clouds.

$15 +$ ⬚ $= 40$

$10 +$ ⬚ $= 19$

⬚ $+ 4 = 12$

4 + ☐ = 29

14 + ☐ = 36

These types of sums are called **equations**.

13 + ☐ = 26

Daft doublers
These crazy aliens only travel in equal numbers!
Double up each type, then write in the totals.

 + = ☐

+ = ☐

Sticker star time!

Challenging times

Some addition sums are set out differently and you have to work out the answer in a different way.

Message in a bottle

Tom Smythe has been stranded on this island for weeks! Read his letter, then write in the correct answers to the questions.

To whoever may find this letter,

Time has passed so slowly on this island, I can't remember when I got here! I made a list of the days:

Warm sunny days	17
Blistering hot days	12
Wet days	24

I often stare out at the ocean, hoping to be saved. Once I saw 3 pirate ships, but they sailed away.

If you find this letter please send help. Only the animals keep me cheerful. I've spotted two whales, and a dozen crabs have tiptoed past me on the sand. I've even seen an octopus waggling his tentacles.

Yours hopefully,

Tom Smythe.

How many days has Tom been on the island in total? ☐

On how many days was there rain? ☐

How many ships have sailed past the island? ☐

Count up all of the animals that Tom has spotted. ☐

Sticker star time!

Bigger and bigger!

You can follow the same rules for adding, no matter how big the numbers get.

Even large two-digit sums are easy when you know how.

Market day

Farmer Brown is counting up the animals he needs to take to the market. Find the correct sticker sums to go with the signs he's put up around the farm.

26 HORSES

55 CHICKENS

38 GEESE

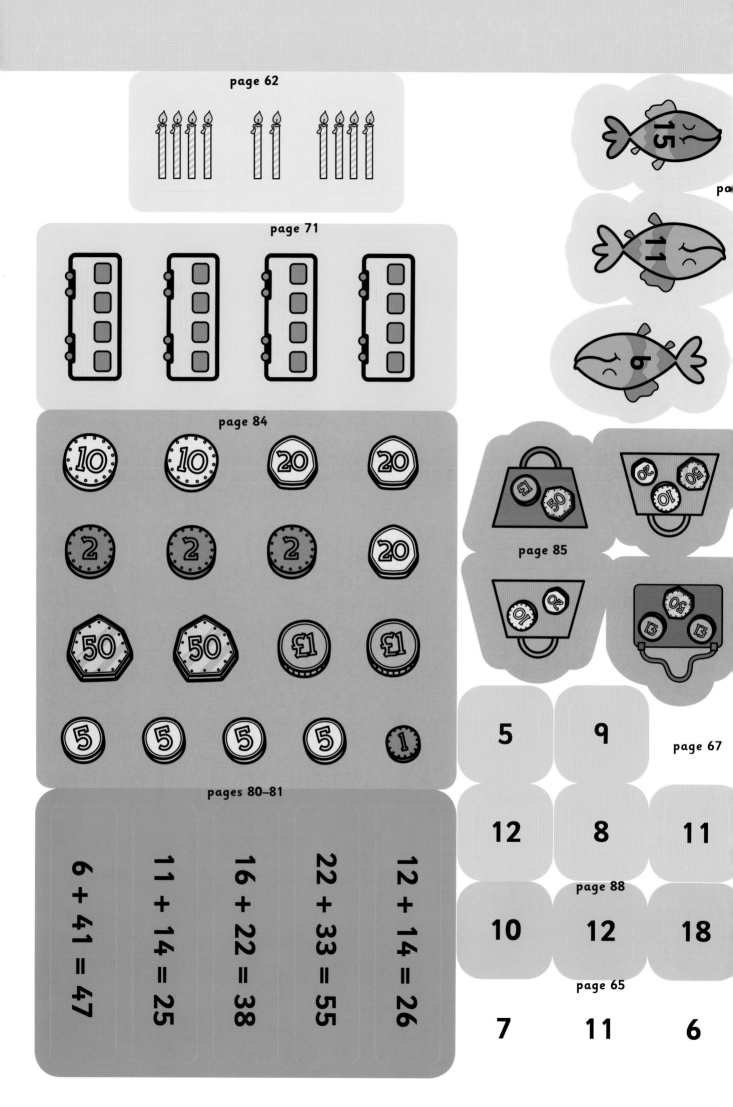

page 62

page 71

page 84

pages 80–81

15

11

9

page 85

5

9

page 67

12

8

11

page 88

10

12

18

page 65

7

11

6

6 + 41 = 47

11 + 14 = 25

16 + 22 = 38

22 + 33 = 55

12 + 14 = 26

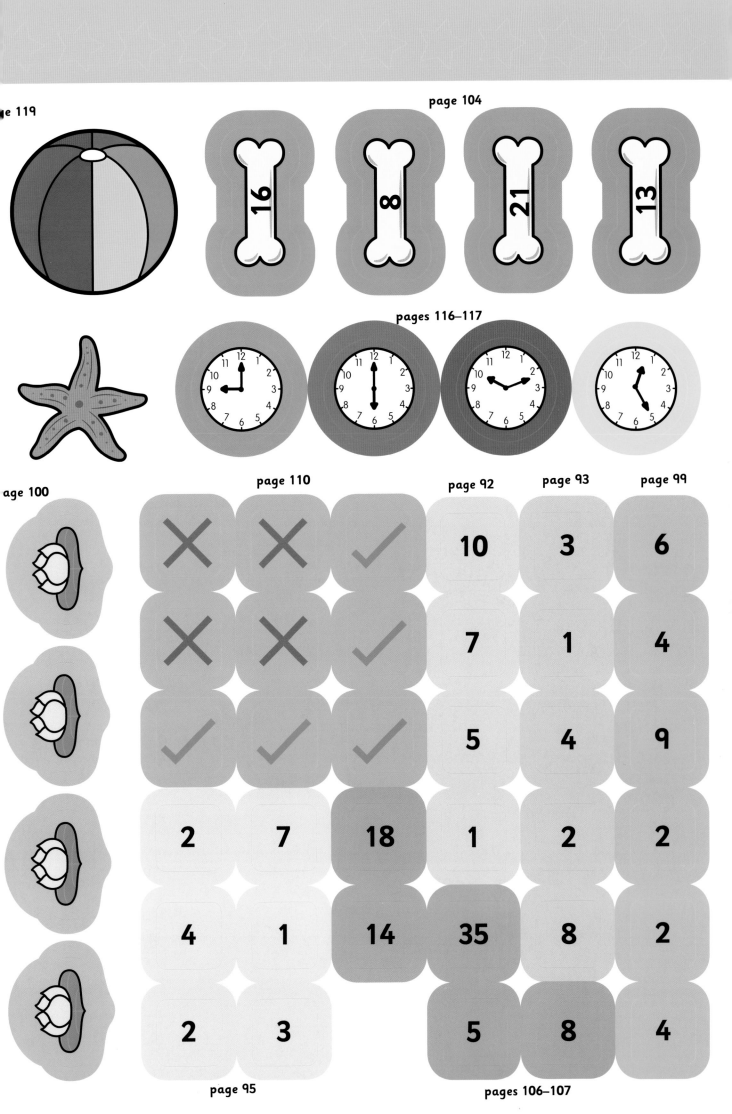

page 119

page 104

16

8

21

13

pages 116–117

age 100

page 110

page 92

page 93

page 99

X X ✓

10 3 6

X X ✓

7 1 4

✓ ✓ ✓

5 4 9

2 7 18

1 2 2

4 1 14

35 8 2

2 3

5 8 4

page 95

pages 106–107

47 COWS

25 PIGS

Counting sheep
Help Farmer Brown count his sheep.
Write your answers in the boxes.

Use a number line to help you count forward to the right answer.

12 + 19 = ☐ lambs

28 + 14 = ☐ ewes

15 + 27 = ☐ rams

Sticker star time!

6 27 28 29 30 31 32 33 34 35 36 37 38 39 40 41 42 43 44 45 46 47 48 49 50

Plus is no fuss

When you are adding large numbers together, try adding the parts separately. This is called **partitioning**.

For example, if you are adding 35 and 27, you can split the numbers up like this:

$(30 + 5) + (20 + 7) = (30 + 20) + (5 + 7) = 50 + 12 = 62$

Work out the sums below. Use another piece of paper for your working out if you need to.

$35 + 7 = \boxed{}$

- - - - - - - - - - - - - - - -

$26 + 24 = \boxed{}$

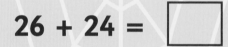

- - - - - - - - - - - - - - - -

$19 + 17 = \boxed{}$

- - - - - - - - - - - - - - - -

$34 + 12 = \boxed{}$

- - - - - - - - - - - - - - - -

1 2 3 4 5 6 7 8 9 10 11 12 13 14 15 16 17 18 19 20 21 22 23 24 2

Number grids

Complete the number grids below.
Stick in a honey pot for every one you finish.

Make each line add up to 18.

3			1	8
2				
		4		3

Try different numbers to see if they work and change them if you need to. Use a piece of paper to jot down your workings.

Make each line add up to 25.

5			4	
				5
8	7			1

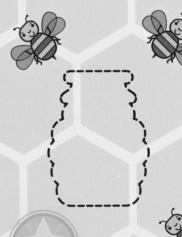

Sticker star time!

Funny money

Food festival!

The children are off to the school food festival. Can you help them work out how much money they need to buy some snacks?

Find the sticker coins to make the exact money to buy each treat.

apple
15p

pizza
55p

juice
18p

spaghetti
£2.45

potato
74p

Put the correct bag sticker next to each child.

Undersea adding game

Play this adding game with up to three friends.

Press the four coloured shell stickers onto some card and then carefully cut them out.
Choose a counter each then find a die to get started.

How to play

Take turns to throw the die, then move forward along the board.

Each of the blue squares has a special challenge. If your fellow voyagers agree that it has been completed successfully, that player may move forward **1 extra square**.

The winner is the first player to get to the desert island!

START
Count up to 10 and back down again without making a mistake.

2

Stop to admire the sea horses. Miss a turn.

Add these coins together

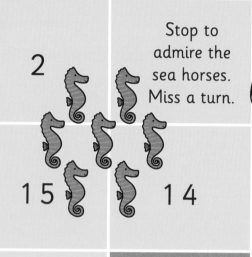

15

14

What is the answer to 95 + 0?

Catch sight of dry land. Take an extra throw.

Name three number pairs for 10.

18

29

Stop to explore a shipwreck. Go back to 22.

27

13 + 6, 14 + 5 and 11 + 8 all equal what number?

31

Lighthouse guides you. Choose a player to miss a turn.

Dolphins lead you in the right direction, move on to 46.

41

Add 17 + 5.

Dive in and swim for the last few metres. Miss a turn.

46

5

Hitch a ride in a submarine. Go forward 3 spaces.

17 sharks plus 2 more equals how many sharks?

8

12

Waste time daydreaming about the island. Go back 6 spaces.

What is 23 + 11?

9

Submarine springs a leak. Pass the die to the player on your left.

20

Waves sweep you forward. Take an extra throw.

22

What is 12 + 21?

What is the sum of 6 and 4?

24

23

33

34

Crab pinches your toe, go back 1 space.

Name three number pairs for 20.

2 dogfish and 2 eels live in a cave. How many creatures in total?

39

Climb aboard a tugboat. Take another throw.

What's the total of £1.53 + £2.10?

Stinging jellyfish! Give all players an extra throw.

23 plus what number equals 31?

FINISH – DRY LAND

Amazing adders quiz

Chocolate challenge
Count up the chocolate chunks then add them together to solve each of the sums.

Pirate problems
Stick in the correct answers before the friendly smile disappears from Old Blackbeard's face.

A pirate boat has 5 sails. How many sails would 2 pirate boats have?

A warship has 4 cannons. How many cannons would 3 warships have in total?

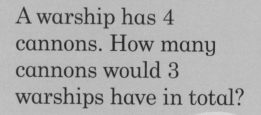

Captain Bluebeard has 4 gold coins, Pirate Pete has 6 coins and Davey Morgan has 8 coins. How many coins do they have altogether?

Eight is great

The answer to each of these sums is 88.
Fill in the blanks to solve the equations below.

14 + ☐ = 88   53 + ☐ = 88

☐ + 62 = 88   ☐ + 19 = 88

45 + ☐ = 88   39 + ☐ = 88

77 + ☐ = 88   ☐ + 1 = 88

Counting crossword

Work out the sums then write the numbers in words to complete the crossword.

Across

1. 1 + 1 + 3 = ☐

2. 9 + 2 + 5 = ☐

3. 2 + 5 + 3 = ☐

4. 4 + 4 + 1 = ☐

Down

1. 2 + 1 + 1 = ☐

2. 3 + 4 + 1 = ☐

3. 7 + 1 + 3 = ☐

4. 2 + 2 + 3 = ☐

5. 5 + 4 + 3 = ☐

Reward chart

Sticker star time!

Use this chart to keep a record of your progress. Give yourself a sticker star when you see 'Sticker star time!' on the page.

 Party puzzlers

 Sums at the shops

 To ten and beyond

 Maths chatter / All the right answers

 Up and down the line

 Playing with numbers

 Swap shop / Adding more and more

 The sky's the limit!

 Challenging times

 Bigger and bigger!

 Plus is no fuss

 Funny money

HOMEWORK HELPERS
Taking Away

Written by Amanda Archer
Illustrated by Ian Cunliffe
Educational Consultant: Geraldine Taylor

Turn back the clocks

Practise counting forward to 20 and back again. When you've cracked counting, taking away is as easy as 3, 2, 1, 0.

Cuckoo counting
Start at number twelve and then count all the way down to zero. Stick in the missing numbers along the way.

12 11 [ ] 9 8 [ ] 6 [ ] 4 3 2 [ ] 0

Walter's wind back
Walter Watch's clocks are missing their little hands. Help him count back to the right numbers then draw the little hands in place.

Count back 2 then draw the little hand on the number 3.

Count back 6 then draw the little hand on the number 1.

Count back 1 then draw the little hand on the number 8.

Fee-fi-fo one!

It's taking Jack a long time to climb down his beanstalk. He keeps stopping for a snack.

When we count one less we are **taking away**.

Cross one snack out each time (the first one has been done for you), then put in a sticker to show how many are left.

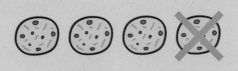 cookies, and 1 less is

 apples, and 1 less is

 bunches of cherries, and 1 less is

 sandwiches, and 1 less is

 sweets, and 1 less is

Sticker star time!

93

Sky-high subtraction

Sometimes when we are counting back, we need to take **two** things away from the total.

Up, up and away

Count up the things that you can see in the sky, then write the number that is two less.

take away 2 leaves [ ]

take away 2 leaves [ ]

take away 2 leaves [ ]

take away 2 leaves [ ]

Royal washing

King Zero wants his laundry to dry in the sun. What happens if he unpegs zero pieces of washing from the line? Write in the answers.

Zero is another word for none.

$$8 - 0 = \boxed{}$$

Rainy runaways

Uh-oh, it's raining!
Some of the animals have run for cover.
How many are left? Look at each sum
then put the right answer sticker in place.

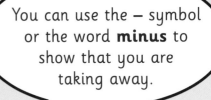

You can use the − symbol or the word **minus** to show that you are taking away.

3 − 1 = [ ]

9 − 2 = [ ]

7 − 3 = [ ]

2 − 1 = [ ]

4 − 2 = [ ]

5 − 2 = [ ]

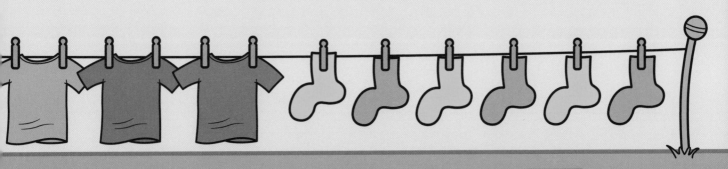

3 − 0 = [ ]

6 − 0 = [ ]

Sticker star time!

Disappearing numbers

Subtraction spells
Wanda the witch is making a powerful magic spell.
Help her subtract the things she needs.

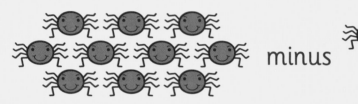

In maths, **subtraction** is another word for taking away.

Fairytale fun
Even princesses need to know how to do subtraction.
Fill in the number grids for this little princess, then
stick a tiara next to every one you complete.

Take away **4**

9	6	7	12	5	10	8	4
5	2						

Take away **3**

5	12	6	9	11	8	4	7
2							

Take away **6**

13	8	10	7	12	14	9	11
7							

96

Nursery numbers

There is only one answer star twinkling next to these nursery rhyme characters, but lots of possible subtractions.

Find two sticker subtractions for each answer star and put them into the scene.

= **10**

When you work out maths in your head, it is called **mental arithmetic**.

= **2**

= **8**

= **6**

= **7**

Sticker star time!

Subtracting spots

Understanding **difference** is part of learning to take away.

Domino difference

Look at the number of spots on each section of the dominoes below. What is the difference between each section? Write your answers in the boxes. The first one has been done for you.

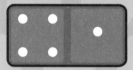 difference = 2   difference =

difference =   difference =

Dotty dice

This tricky dice activity will test your adding skills, too.

Add up the spots that you can see on each die, then find the difference between the totals.

> The word **difference** means that you must take the smaller number away from the bigger number. The answer is the difference between the two numbers.

The total of

+ + =   + + =

☐ − ☐ = ☐

The total of

+ + =   + + =

☐ − ☐ = ☐

count back 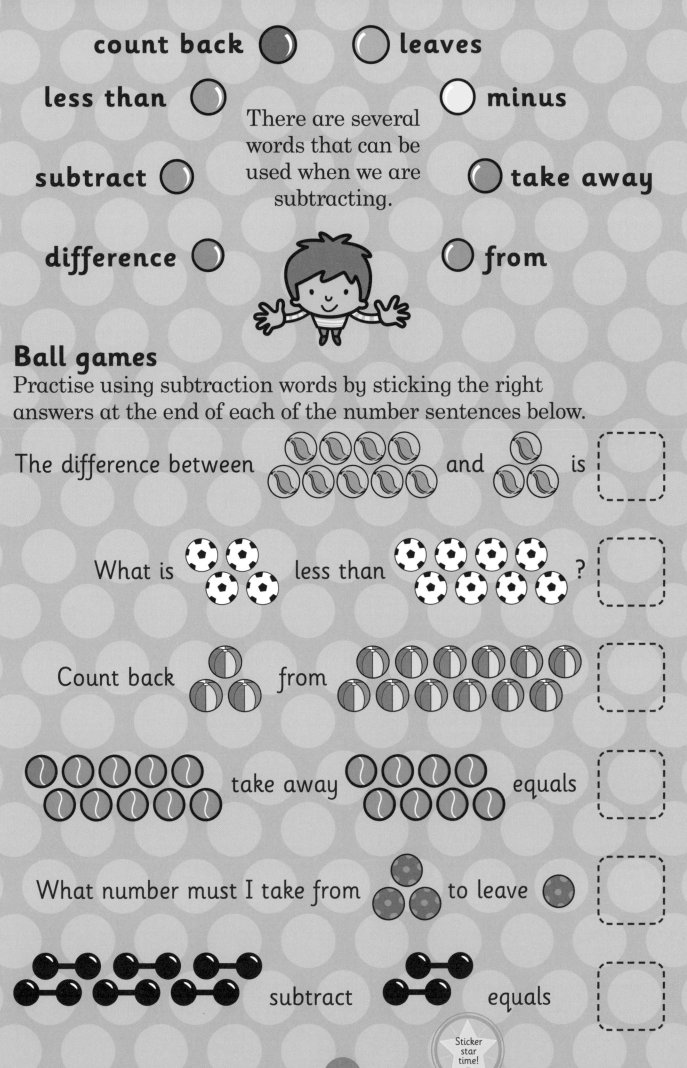 leaves

less than minus

subtract There are several words that can be used when we are subtracting. take away

difference from

Ball games

Practise using subtraction words by sticking the right answers at the end of each of the number sentences below.

The difference between and is

What is less than ?

Count back from

take away equals

What number must I take from to leave

subtract equals

Sticker star time!

99

Learning to leapfrog

Number lines can help us with subtraction.
One way to use a number line is to count backwards. To take away using a number line, put your finger on the bigger number then count back the smaller number. When you finish counting, you have reached your answer.

Hop to the spot
Look at the sums below. Now, count your way back to the correct stepping stone. Put a lily pad sticker next to the answer each time.

22 – 7

18 – 6

12 – 9

25 – 5

Bigger jumps backwards

When you are working with harder subtractions, try counting up from the smaller number to the bigger number to work out the difference between them.

Use the number line at the top of the page then write down the answers to these two-digit sums.

12 – 10 = ☐

18 – 14 = ☐

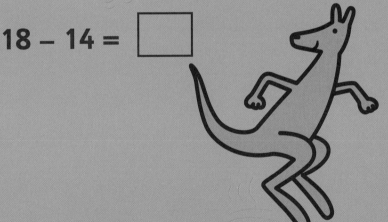

You can work out subtractions like this:
44 – 26 = (44 – 20) – 6 = 24 – 6 = 18

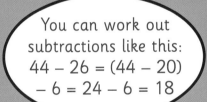

25 – 19 = ☐

49 – 21 = ☐

38 – 23 = ☐

Sticker star time!

Money matters

Taking away can be very useful when you're out shopping. If you find money calculations hard, try counting with real coins.

All change

Write down the change from 10p that you would get for each of these items.

8p

☐ **p change**

5p

☐ **p change**

2p

☐ **p change**

4p

☐ **p change**

9p

☐ **p change**

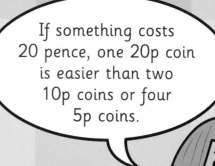

If something costs 20 pence, one 20p coin is easier than two 10p coins or four 5p coins.

Twenty pence price challenge

If you paid for each of these items with a 20p coin, how much change would you get?

5p

change = ◯

18p

change = ◯

17p

change = ◯

13p

change = ◯

15p

change = ◯

10p

change = ◯

I've only got a 10p coin. Do I have enough for the blue jumper?

I've used my 20p to buy this scarf. Can I afford anything else with the change?

Sticker star time!

Daft dogs

Hungry pups

Look at the subtractions along the trails of paw prints. There's only one answer bone for each pet. Find the right one and then stick it in each dog's bowl.

   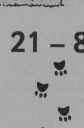

20 – 4	48 – 27	37 – 29	21 – 8
23 – 7	30 – 9	46 – 38	43 – 30
32 – 16	27 – 6	39 – 31	28 – 15
45 – 29	36 – 15	22 – 14	17 – 4

 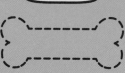 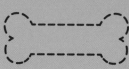

FIFI   SPOT   SCRUFFY   BRUISER

The right and the wrong way

Now that you're a whiz at simple subtraction, what happens if you turn things around?

Subtraction calculations have to start with the bigger number.

Put a tick next to the correct subtraction calculation and a cross next to the one that's not right.

8 – 5 = 3 ☐   5 – 8 = 3 ☐

Purr-fect opposites

The rules for setting out adding and subtraction are useful when we are trying to find missing numbers in the middle of a calculation. Write the missing numbers in the boxes.

To find the missing number, turn the subtraction around to make an addition question.

23 – ☐ = 15

15 + ☐ = 23

Now try a few more.

18 – ☐ = 11   29 – ☐ = 13   24 – ☐ = 19

11 + ☐ = 18   13 + ☐ = 29   19 + ☐ = 24

When you subtract numbers close to multiples of 10, such as 11, 19 or 29, subtract the closest multiple of 10, then add or subtract 1. For example:
74 – 29 = 74 – 30 + 1 = 44 + 1 = 45

Sticker star time!

Underwater equations

Use your maths skills to write the missing numbers in these subtractions. If you find adding up easier, then turn the numbers around to create an addition sum.

Daring diving

When the diver swam into this coral reef, lots of sea creatures disappeared!
Stick in the correct number to show how many of each of the animals were brave enough to stay.

46 − [ ] = 11 **dolphins stayed**

These types of maths problems are called **equations**.

17 − [ ] = 9

seahorses stayed

Add the submarine stickers to the scene.

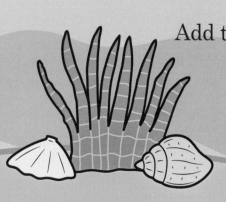

41 – ☐ = 36

fish stayed

34 – ☐ = 16

starfish stayed

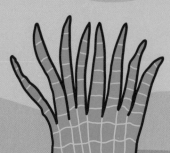

29 – ☐ = 15

crabs stayed

Jiggly jellyfish

These jellyfish have lots of tentacles between them. Count up the total number of tentacles in each group and work out what **half** that number is.

The blue jellyfish have ___ tentacles. Half of ___ is ____.

The green jellyfish have ___ tentacles. Half of ___ is ____.

The purple jellyfish have ___ tentacles. Half of ___ is ____.

Sticker star time!

Pen pal problems

A visit from Vanessa
Read Vanessa's letter to Kai, then write in the answers to the questions below.

Dear Kai,

I'm in the school show! We're performing Puss in Boots. There are 50 pupils in the show altogether.

This morning I bought lots of things for my trip to see you. I bought a reading book for 30p, a jumper for 70p, a card game for 25p and a pair of gloves for 45p.

I also bought my bus ticket. Usually, there are 8 buses each day to your town. On the day I'm coming however, 3 buses have been cancelled.

From,
Vanessa x

How many children are in the school show? ____

What's the difference between the cheapest and the most expensive items she bought? ____

How much more were the gloves than the reading book? _____

How many buses will be running on the day of Vanessa's trip? _____

Kai's sticker sums

Find the stickers to answer the questions underneath Kai's postcard.

These subtraction questions show us how we all use maths in our everyday life.

Hey Vanessa!

The only photo I can find for you has too many people in it. My sister and I, and Mum and Dad, were at a wedding when 11 of my cousins joined the shot!

We had a garage sale in the front garden. I sold 19 things on Saturday, 13 on Sunday and 5 things on Monday.

My dad will pick you up from the bus station. It's 9km away, but he knows a short cut that's only 5km.

Love, Kai

How many people are in the photo Kai found?

What's the difference between the number of items sold on Kai's best garage sale day and his worst?

How many more things did Kai sell on Sunday compared to Monday?

How many kilometres does Kai's dad save with his shortcut to the bus station?

sticker star time!

Jungle japes

The rules for subtracting will always lead you back to the correct answers, no matter how big the numbers get.

Big game test
The animals have worked out some correct answers and some incorrect answers. Can you spot which is which?

Sort out the subtractions by putting in tick and cross stickers next to each one.

81 – 58 = 23

56 – 47 = 13

70 – 44 = 26

56 – 44 = 12

99 – 33 = 54

28 – 17 = 11

45 – 16 = 28

39 – 21 = 19

44 – 12 = 32

Bird brain-teasers

When you are taking away 2 digit numbers, you might find that the units you are taking away are bigger than the units you are taking away from.

When this happens, you need to take the tens away first. Then you can take the units away.
For example:

42 – 16 = 26

42 – 16 (42 – 10) – 6 = 32 – 6 = 26

This is called **partitioning**.

Here are a few subtractions for you to try.

Write your answers on the page and then stick a picture of Tony Toucan next to each one you finish. You can use another piece of paper to jot things down if you need to.

51 – 38 =

72 – 25 =

93 – 56 =

If you're finding big subtractions tricky, don't forget that you can use a number line to help you.

Sticker star time!

Subtraction chains

Sometimes in maths we need to take away a whole series of numbers from one total. Work your way steadily through the calculations to get to the right answer.

Learning ladders

Have a go at these long equations and fill in the spaces in the ladders. Then write down the answer for each ladder.

73	49	52	68
− 9	− 18	− 31	− 23
− 20	− 5	− 8	− 17
− 6	− 12	− 8	− 26
=	=	=	=

pages 76–77

page 86

page 67

page 72

pages 76–77

page 63

page 72

page 111

page 96

page 106

page 115

page 97

13 – 3

14 – 4

10 – 2

14 – 12

14 – 6

9 – 7

15 – 9

12 – 6

11 – 4

8 – 1

page 109

14

4

15

8

page 103

5

50

£1

20

£1

£1

£1

£1

£1

£1

£1

£1

50

1

10

10

5

5

5

2

2

2

1

Mental maths

Crazy code breaker

Break the code on the computer by using subtraction to complete the key on the screen.

Write down the correct number for each letter, then unscramble the message below.

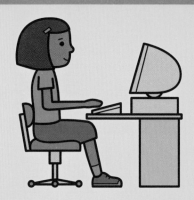

A = 12 – 4 ☐   N = 39 – 23 ☐
B = 56 – 43 ☐   O = 52 – 38 ☐
C = 75 – 54 ☐   P = 37 – 36 ☐
D = 64 – 60 ☐   Q = 75 – 63 ☐
E = 50 – 32 ☐   R = 16 – 13 ☐
F = 75 – 50 ☐   S = 45 – 30 ☐
G = 47 – 23 ☐   T = 57 – 35 ☐
H = 86 – 77 ☐   U = 34 – 17 ☐
I = 13 – 11 ☐   V = 48 – 43 ☐
J = 68 – 57 ☐   W = 30 – 7 ☐
K = 54 – 34 ☐   X = 67 – 57 ☐
L = 96 – 90 ☐   Y = 85 – 78 ☐
M = 46 – 20 ☐   Z = 26 – 7 ☐

2 / 21 14 17 6 4 / 22 8 20 18 / 8 23 8 7 / 8 6 6 / 4 8 7!

The message is...

_ _ _ _ _ _   _ _ _ _   _ _ _ _   _ _ _   _ _ _!

Sticker star time!

Transport teasers

You've been dropped off at the airport. Now you need to work out where you would like to go.

Find a flight
Take a look at the airline price list, then write in the answers to the maths problems below.

MANCHESTER	£40
GLASGOW	£79
LONDON	£33
EXETER	£62
EDINBURGH	£95

You've got £75. Where **can't** you go? _____
and _____

If you go to London, how much change will you have? _____

What's the difference between the most expensive and the cheapest flights? _____

If you save £30 of your money for presents, which two flights could you still choose from? _____ and _____

The Manchester flight is full. If you go to London instead, how much money will you save? _____

You've chosen a flight that is £33 cheaper than the flight to Edinburgh. Write your final destination in here.

ONE TICKET TO _ _ _ _ _ _ _

Holiday shopping

Now your flight is booked, it's time to buy some goodies for the journey.
Use the coin stickers to put in the change you would get from a £5 note.

**book
£4.45**

**playing cards
£3.00**

When you are buying something, there can be several combinations of coins that work.

**sandwiches
99p**

**sweets
£1.30**

Sticker star time!

The dawn-till-dusk race

START – RISE AND SHINE

7 o'clock – Give your teeth a good brush. Take an extra throw.

What is less than

15

9 o'clock – run all the way to school. Take an extra throw.

Play this game with up to three other friends. Everything seems to be happening at super-speed this morning – which of you can get through the day and back into bed again first? Press the four clock stickers onto some card and then carefully cut them out. Choose a counter each, then find a die to get started.

Which sum is incorrect?
25 – 12 = 13
34 – 12 = 29
53 – 12 = 41

You're th last to fin your spelli take 2 off next dice th

29

28

Do a grea abstract painting in Move on 34.

How to play

Take turns to throw the die, then move along the board. Each yellow taking away square has a special challenge. If the other players agree that it has been completed successfully, the player may move forward 1 extra square. The winner is the player that is tucked up in bed before the rest!

What number must I take from 27 to leave 5?

3 o'clock – Home time! Wait ages for a bus. Go back to 28.

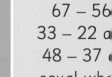

67 – 56
33 – 22 a
48 – 37
equal who

Squeeze in a quick game of football before tea. Take an extra throw.

Have a lo family dinn Go back t 35.

Does 97 – 79 = 20?

5

8 o'clock – Your zip gets stuck. Go back to square 5.

9 – 7, 11 – 9 and 5 – 3 all equal what number?

What is 23 minus 14?

Wave to your mum. Take a throw instead of the player to your right.

9

You buy six penny sweets, what change do you get from ten pence?

20

21

What's the difference between each half of this domino?

Count back 17 from 46.

Everything stops for lunch. Give all of your opponents double turns.

Subtract 97 from 100.

34

35

Help Mum do her shopping. Score 6 for your next throw.

40

Really easy homework tonight, skip on to 42.

Does £3.20 – £2.40 equal £1.20?

37

What's the difference between 112 and 75?

48

8 o'clock – Toothbrush time again! Take another throw.

FINISH – NIGHT NIGHT!

Super subtracters' quiz

Split the difference

Look at these sets of farmyard animals. What is the number difference between the herd on the left and the herd on the right?

  **difference** [ ]

  **difference** [ ]

Subtraction action

Work out the correct answers and write them in the boxes.

88 – 63 = [ ]   96 – 45 = [ ]

64 – 24 = [ ]   19 – 13 = [ ]

Test your mental arithmetic by filling in the two subtraction grids belo

Take away 9

14	67	38	85	92	28	74	31	45	48
5									

Take away 18

76	48	39	20	57	97	84	34	19	72
58									

Bonny beach game

Who's having fun on the beach today? Put a pencil on the first dot, then use your subtraction skills to connect to the next one in the sequence. Keep going until the picture's finished.

16 – 5 •
14 – 2
• 17 – 4
20 – 10
23 – 9
11 – 2 •
• 25 – 10
15 – 7
24 – 8
20 – 3
10 – 3
• 23 – 5
• 20 – 14
21 – 2
12 – 8 23 – 3
13 – 8
• 5 – 3
7 – 4
1

When you've joined up the dots, colour in the sunny scene.
Now stick a beach ball and a starfish into the picture.

Reward chart

Sticker star time!

Use this chart to keep a record of your progress. Each time you see the 'Sticker star time' sign, add a star to the chart.

☆ **Turn back the clocks**

☆ **Sky-high subtraction**

☆ **Disappearing numbers**

☆ **Subtracting spots**

☆ **Learning to leapfrog**

☆ **Money matters**

☆ **Daft dogs**

☆ **Underwater equations**

☆ **Pen pal problems**

☆ **Jungle japes**

☆ **Subtraction chains / Mental maths**

☆ **Transport teasers**

HOMEWORK HELPERS

Times Tables

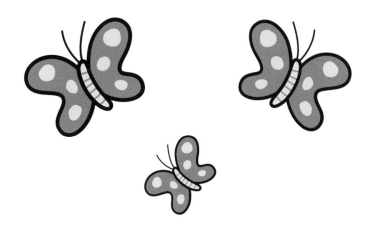

Illustrated by Ian Cunliffe

1 Times Table

0 x 1 = 0
1 x 1 = 1
2 x 1 = 2
3 x 1 = 3
4 x 1 = 4
5 x 1 = 5
6 x 1 = 6
7 x 1 = 7
8 x 1 = 8
9 x 1 = 9
10 x 1 = 10
11 x 1 = 11
12 x 1 = 12

One naughty elephant!

1 – one 1st – first

Word | Meaning

Word	Meaning
single	one, on its own
unicycle	one-wheeled cycle
solo	for one person
once	one time

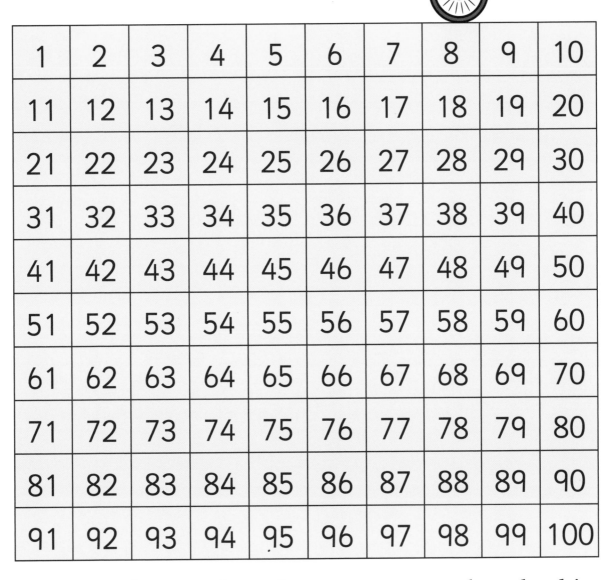

Here are the numbers from one to one hundred in a number grid. This shows the one times table.

2 Times Table

How many fish
can we catch?

$0 \times 2 = 0$

$1 \times 2 = 2$

$2 \times 2 = 4$

$3 \times 2 = 6$

$4 \times 2 = 8$

$5 \times 2 = 10$

$6 \times 2 = 12$

$7 \times 2 = 14$

$8 \times 2 = 16$

$9 \times 2 = 18$

$10 \times 2 = 20$

$11 \times 2 = 22$

$12 \times 2 = 24$

2 – two   2nd – second

Word	Meaning
double	two times as much
pair	two matching items
bicycle	two-wheeled cycle
twice	two times
twins	two children born at the same time

1	2	3	4	5	6	7	8	9	10
11	12	13	14	15	16	17	18	19	20
21	22	23	24	25	26	27	28	29	30
31	32	33	34	35	36	37	38	39	40
41	42	43	44	45	46	47	48	49	50
51	52	53	54	55	56	57	58	59	60
61	62	63	64	65	66	67	68	69	70
71	72	73	74	75	76	77	78	79	80
81	82	83	84	85	86	87	88	89	90
91	92	93	94	95	96	97	98	99	100

The numbers in blue show the pattern of the two times table. What do you notice about the numbers in the blue columns?

3 Times Table

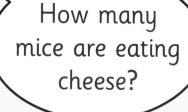

How many mice are eating cheese?

$0 \times 3 = 0$

$1 \times 3 = 3$

$2 \times 3 = 6$

$3 \times 3 = 9$

$4 \times 3 = 12$

$5 \times 3 = 15$

$6 \times 3 = 18$

$7 \times 3 = 21$

$8 \times 3 = 24$

$9 \times 3 = 27$

$10 \times 3 = 30$

$11 \times 3 = 33$

$12 \times 3 = 36$

3 – three   3rd – third

Word

triple, treble

tricycle

triangle

trilogy

triplets

Meaning

three times as much

three-wheeled cycle

three-sided flat shape

three-part book, play or film

three children born at the same time

1	2	3	4	5	6	7	8	9	10
11	12	13	14	15	16	17	18	19	20
21	22	23	24	25	26	27	28	29	30
31	32	33	34	35	36	37	38	39	40
41	42	43	44	45	46	47	48	49	50
51	52	53	54	55	56	57	58	59	60
61	62	63	64	65	66	67	68	69	70
71	72	73	74	75	76	77	78	79	80
81	82	83	84	85	86	87	88	89	90
91	92	93	94	95	96	97	98	99	100

The numbers in red show the pattern of the three times table. What do you notice about the red numbers going downwards?

4 Times Table

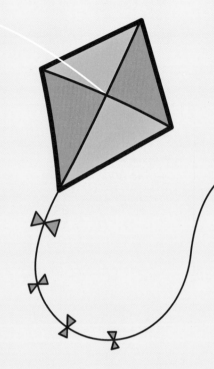

0 x 4 =   0
1 x 4 =   4
2 x 4 =   8
3 x 4 = 12
4 x 4 = 16
5 x 4 = 20
6 x 4 = 24
7 x 4 = 28
8 x 4 = 32
9 x 4 = 36
10 x 4 = 40
11 x 4 = 44
12 x 4 = 48

How many sides does my kite have?

4 – four 4th – fourth

Word   **Meaning**

quadruple   four times as much

quarter   one of four equal
parts of a whole

square   a flat shape with four equal sides

quadruplets   four children born at the same time

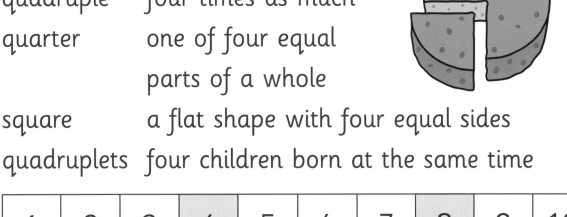

1	2	3	4	5	6	7	8	9	10
11	12	13	14	15	16	17	18	19	20
21	22	23	24	25	26	27	28	29	30
31	32	33	34	35	36	37	38	39	40
41	42	43	44	45	46	47	48	49	50
51	52	53	54	55	56	57	58	59	60
61	62	63	64	65	66	67	68	69	70
71	72	73	74	75	76	77	78	79	80
81	82	83	84	85	86	87	88	89	90
91	92	93	94	95	96	97	98	99	100

The numbers in orange show the four times table.
What do you notice about it?

Does it remind you of the two times table?

5 Times Table

0 x 5 =   0

1 x 5 =   5

2 x 5 = 10

3 x 5 = 15

4 x 5 = 20

5 x 5 = 25

6 x 5 = 30

7 x 5 = 35

8 x 5 = 40

9 x 5 = 45

10 x 5 = 50

11 x 5 = 55

12 x 5 = 60

How many stars are in the sky?

5 – five 5th – fifth

Word   **Meaning**

quintuple   five times as much

pentagon   a shape with five sides

quintet   five singers or musicians

pentathlon   an athletics contest with five events

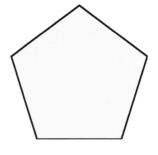

1	2	3	4	5	6	7	8	9	10
11	12	13	14	15	16	17	18	19	20
21	22	23	24	25	26	27	28	29	30
31	32	33	34	35	36	37	38	39	40
41	42	43	44	45	46	47	48	49	50
51	52	53	54	55	56	57	58	59	60
61	62	63	64	65	66	67	68	69	70
71	72	73	74	75	76	77	78	79	80
81	82	83	84	85	86	87	88	89	90
91	92	93	94	95	96	97	98	99	100

The numbers in yellow show the five times table.
Look at the yellow columns. Do you notice anything
about the units?

6 Times Table

$$0 \times 6 = 0$$
$$1 \times 6 = 6$$
$$2 \times 6 = 12$$
$$3 \times 6 = 18$$
$$4 \times 6 = 24$$
$$5 \times 6 = 30$$
$$6 \times 6 = 36$$
$$7 \times 6 = 42$$
$$8 \times 6 = 48$$
$$9 \times 6 = 54$$
$$10 \times 6 = 60$$
$$11 \times 6 = 66$$
$$12 \times 6 = 72$$

How many spots does each butterfly have?

6 – six 6ᵗʰ – sixth

Word	Meaning
sextuple	six times as much
hexagon	a flat shape with six equal sides
sextuplets	six children born at the same time
sextet	six singers or musicians

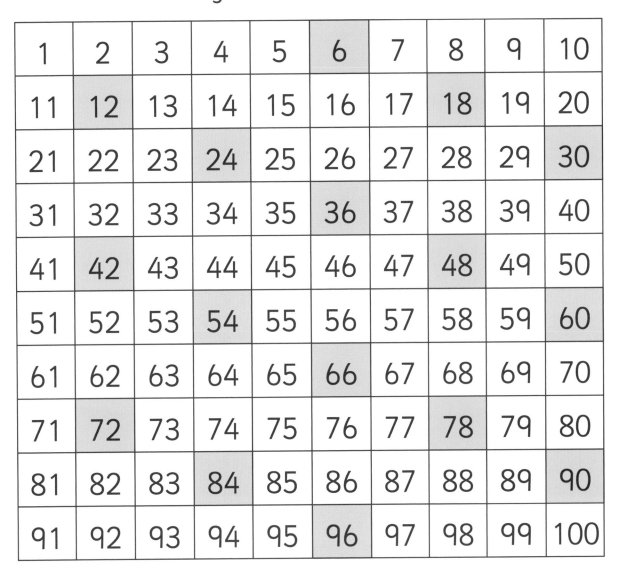

1	2	3	4	5	6	7	8	9	10
11	12	13	14	15	16	17	18	19	20
21	22	23	24	25	26	27	28	29	30
31	32	33	34	35	36	37	38	39	40
41	42	43	44	45	46	47	48	49	50
51	52	53	54	55	56	57	58	59	60
61	62	63	64	65	66	67	68	69	70
71	72	73	74	75	76	77	78	79	80
81	82	83	84	85	86	87	88	89	90
91	92	93	94	95	96	97	98	99	100

The numbers in green show the six times table. What is the pattern of the numbers in the green squares?

133

7 Times Table

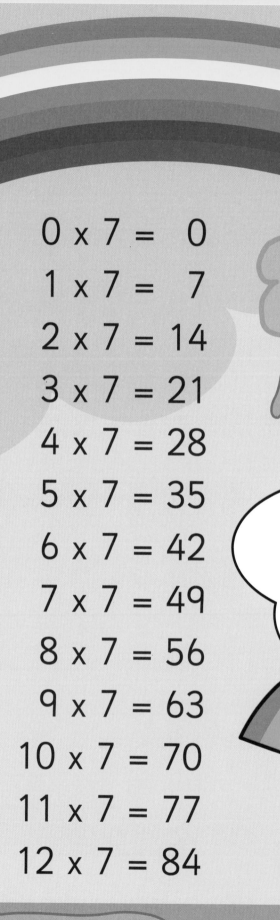

$$0 \times 7 = 0$$
$$1 \times 7 = 7$$
$$2 \times 7 = 14$$
$$3 \times 7 = 21$$
$$4 \times 7 = 28$$
$$5 \times 7 = 35$$
$$6 \times 7 = 42$$
$$7 \times 7 = 49$$
$$8 \times 7 = 56$$
$$9 \times 7 = 63$$
$$10 \times 7 = 70$$
$$11 \times 7 = 77$$
$$12 \times 7 = 84$$

7 – seven 7th – seventh

Word	Meaning
September	in Roman times, this was the seventh month of the year
septennial	lasting for seven years
heptagon	a seven-sided flat shape
septet	seven singers or musicians

1	2	3	4	5	6	7	8	9	10
11	12	13	14	15	16	17	18	19	20
21	22	23	24	25	26	27	28	29	30
31	32	33	34	35	36	37	38	39	40
41	42	43	44	45	46	47	48	49	50
51	52	53	54	55	56	57	58	59	60
61	62	63	64	65	66	67	68	69	70
71	72	73	74	75	76	77	78	79	80
81	82	83	84	85	86	87	88	89	90
91	92	93	94	95	96	97	98	99	100

The numbers in yellow show the pattern of the seven times table. What do you notice this time?

8 Times Table

$$0 \times 8 = 0$$
$$1 \times 8 = 8$$
$$2 \times 8 = 16$$
$$3 \times 8 = 24$$
$$4 \times 8 = 32$$
$$5 \times 8 = 40$$
$$6 \times 8 = 48$$
$$7 \times 8 = 56$$
$$8 \times 8 = 64$$
$$9 \times 8 = 72$$
$$10 \times 8 = 80$$
$$11 \times 8 = 88$$
$$12 \times 8 = 96$$

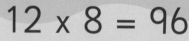

How many tentacles does an octopus have?

8 – eight 8th – eighth

Word	Meaning
October	in Roman times, this was the eighth month of the year
octagon	an eight-sided flat shape
octopus	a sea creature with eight tentacles
octet	eight singers or musicians

1	2	3	4	5	6	7	8	9	10
11	12	13	14	15	16	17	18	19	20
21	22	23	24	25	26	27	28	29	30
31	32	33	34	35	36	37	38	39	40
41	42	43	44	45	46	47	48	49	50
51	52	53	54	55	56	57	58	59	60
61	62	63	64	65	66	67	68	69	70
71	72	73	74	75	76	77	78	79	80
81	82	83	84	85	86	87	88	89	90
91	92	93	94	95	96	97	98	99	100

The numbers in blue show the pattern of the eight times table. Can you see a pattern in the numbers below the blue squares?

9 Times Table

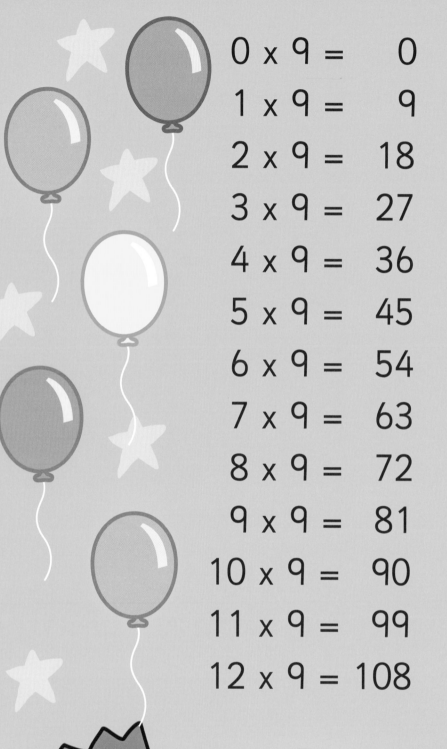

$0 \times 9 = 0$

$1 \times 9 = 9$

$2 \times 9 = 18$

$3 \times 9 = 27$

$4 \times 9 = 36$

$5 \times 9 = 45$

$6 \times 9 = 54$

$7 \times 9 = 63$

$8 \times 9 = 72$

$9 \times 9 = 81$

$10 \times 9 = 90$

$11 \times 9 = 99$

$12 \times 9 = 108$

How old am I today?

9

9 – nine 9th – ninth

Word	Meaning
November	in Roman times, this was the ninth month of the year
nonagon	nine-sided flat shape
nonet	nine singers or musicians

1	2	3	4	5	6	7	8	9	10
11	12	13	14	15	16	17	18	19	20
21	22	23	24	25	26	27	28	29	30
31	32	33	34	35	36	37	38	39	40
41	42	43	44	45	46	47	48	49	50
51	52	53	54	55	56	57	58	59	60
61	62	63	64	65	66	67	68	69	70
71	72	73	74	75	76	77	78	79	80
81	82	83	84	85	86	87	88	89	90
91	92	93	94	95	96	97	98	99	100

The numbers in pink show the pattern of the nine times table. What is the pattern of the tens? What is the pattern of the units?

139

10 Times Table

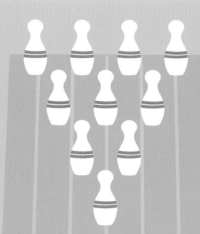

$$0 \times 10 = 0$$
$$1 \times 10 = 10$$
$$2 \times 10 = 20$$
$$3 \times 10 = 30$$
$$4 \times 10 = 40$$
$$5 \times 10 = 50$$
$$6 \times 10 = 60$$
$$7 \times 10 = 70$$
$$8 \times 10 = 80$$
$$9 \times 10 = 90$$
$$10 \times 10 = 100$$
$$11 \times 10 = 110$$
$$12 \times 10 = 120$$

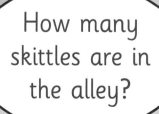

How many skittles are in the alley?

10 – ten 10th – tenth

Word   **Meaning**

December   in Roman times, this was the tenth month

decade   ten years

decagon   ten-sided shape

decathlon   an athletic contest
             with ten events

1	2	3	4	5	6	7	8	9	10
11	12	13	14	15	16	17	18	19	20
21	22	23	24	25	26	27	28	29	30
31	32	33	34	35	36	37	38	39	40
41	42	43	44	45	46	47	48	49	50
51	52	53	54	55	56	57	58	59	60
61	62	63	64	65	66	67	68	69	70
71	72	73	74	75	76	77	78	79	80
81	82	83	84	85	86	87	88	89	90
91	92	93	94	95	96	97	98	99	100

The numbers in blue show the ten times table.
What is the pattern of the tens?
What is the pattern of the units?

11 Times Table

$$0 \times 11 = 0$$
$$1 \times 11 = 11$$
$$2 \times 11 = 22$$
$$3 \times 11 = 33$$
$$4 \times 11 = 44$$
$$5 \times 11 = 55$$
$$6 \times 11 = 66$$
$$7 \times 11 = 77$$
$$8 \times 11 = 88$$
$$9 \times 11 = 99$$
$$10 \times 11 = 110$$
$$11 \times 11 = 121$$
$$12 \times 11 = 132$$

11 – eleven 11th – eleventh

Word

hendecagon

Meaning

eleven-sided flat shape

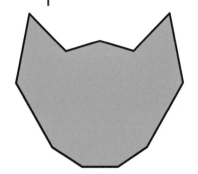

1	2	3	4	5	6	7	8	9	10
11	12	13	14	15	16	17	18	19	20
21	22	23	24	25	26	27	28	29	30
31	32	33	34	35	36	37	38	39	40
41	42	43	44	45	46	47	48	49	50
51	52	53	54	55	56	57	58	59	60
61	62	63	64	65	66	67	68	69	70
71	72	73	74	75	76	77	78	79	80
81	82	83	84	85	86	87	88	89	90
91	92	93	94	95	96	97	98	99	100

The numbers in green show the eleven times table.
What do you notice about the tens and units?
Can you see a link with the one times table?

143

12 Times Table

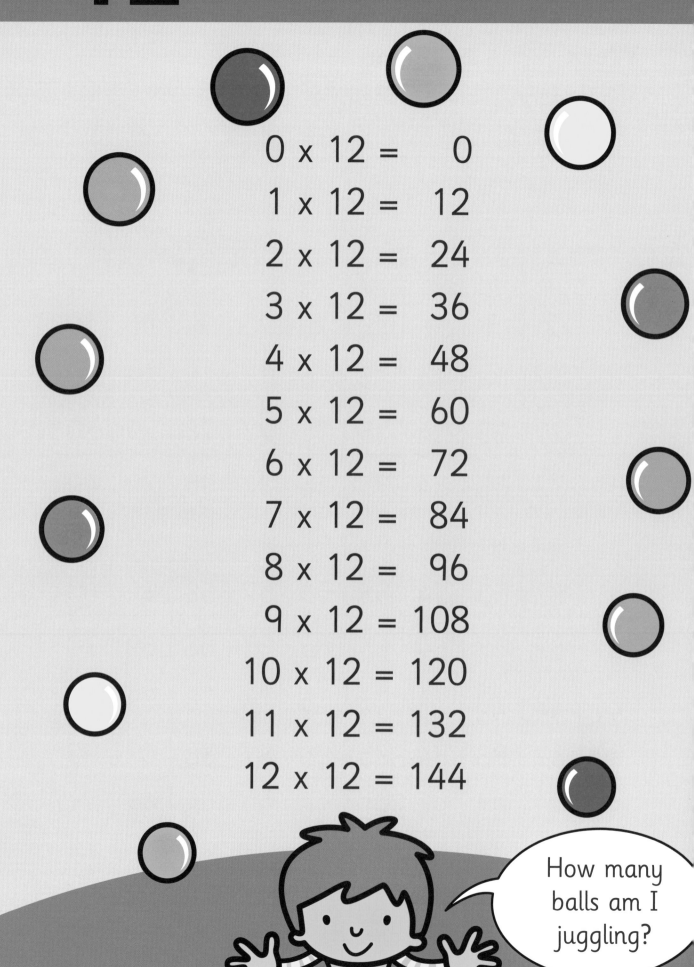

0 x 12 = 0
1 x 12 = 12
2 x 12 = 24
3 x 12 = 36
4 x 12 = 48
5 x 12 = 60
6 x 12 = 72
7 x 12 = 84
8 x 12 = 96
9 x 12 = 108
10 x 12 = 120
11 x 12 = 132
12 x 12 = 144

How many balls am I juggling?

12 – twelve 12th – twelfth

Word	Meaning
dodecagon	twelve-sided flat shape
dozen	twelve of something

1	2	3	4	5	6	7	8	9	10
11	12	13	14	15	16	17	18	19	20
21	22	23	24	25	26	27	28	29	30
31	32	33	34	35	36	37	38	39	40
41	42	43	44	45	46	47	48	49	50
51	52	53	54	55	56	57	58	59	60
61	62	63	64	65	66	67	68	69	70
71	72	73	74	75	76	77	78	79	80
81	82	83	84	85	86	87	88	89	90
91	92	93	94	95	96	97	98	99	100

The numbers in purple show the twelve times table.
What is the pattern of the numbers this time?

1 Times Table

0 x 1 = 0
1 x 1 = 1
2 x 1 = 2
3 x 1 = 3
4 x 1 = 4
5 x 1 = 5
6 x 1 = 6
7 x 1 = 7
8 x 1 = 8
9 x 1 = 9
10 x 1 = 10
11 x 1 = 11
12 x 1 = 12

2 Times Table

0 x 2 = 0
1 x 2 = 2
2 x 2 = 4
3 x 2 = 6
4 x 2 = 8
5 x 2 = 10
6 x 2 = 12
7 x 2 = 14
8 x 2 = 16
9 x 2 = 18
10 x 2 = 20
11 x 2 = 22
12 x 2 = 24

3 Times Table

0 x 3 = 0
1 x 3 = 3
2 x 3 = 6
3 x 3 = 9
4 x 3 = 12
5 x 3 = 15
6 x 3 = 18
7 x 3 = 21
8 x 3 = 24
9 x 3 = 27
10 x 3 = 30
11 x 3 = 33
12 x 3 = 36

7 Times Table

0 x 7 = 0
1 x 7 = 7
2 x 7 = 14
3 x 7 = 21
4 x 7 = 28
5 x 7 = 35
6 x 7 = 42
7 x 7 = 49
8 x 7 = 56
9 x 7 = 63
10 x 7 = 70
11 x 7 = 77
12 x 7 = 84

8 Times Table

0 x 8 = 0
1 x 8 = 8
2 x 8 = 16
3 x 8 = 24
4 x 8 = 32
5 x 8 = 40
6 x 8 = 48
7 x 8 = 56
8 x 8 = 64
9 x 8 = 72
10 x 8 = 80
11 x 8 = 88
12 x 8 = 96

9 Times Table

0 x 9 = 0
1 x 9 = 9
2 x 9 = 18
3 x 9 = 27
4 x 9 = 36
5 x 9 = 45
6 x 9 = 54
7 x 9 = 63
8 x 9 = 72
9 x 9 = 81
10 x 9 = 90
11 x 9 = 99
12 x 9 = 108

4 Times Table

0 x 4 = 0
1 x 4 = 4
2 x 4 = 8
3 x 4 = 12
4 x 4 = 16
5 x 4 = 20
6 x 4 = 24
7 x 4 = 28
8 x 4 = 32
9 x 4 = 36
10 x 4 = 40
11 x 4 = 44
12 x 4 = 48

5 Times Table

0 x 5 = 0
1 x 5 = 5
2 x 5 = 10
3 x 5 = 15
4 x 5 = 20
5 x 5 = 25
6 x 5 = 30
7 x 5 = 35
8 x 5 = 40
9 x 5 = 45
10 x 5 = 50
11 x 5 = 55
12 x 5 = 60

6 Times Table

0 x 6 = 0
1 x 6 = 6
2 x 6 = 12
3 x 6 = 18
4 x 6 = 24
5 x 6 = 30
6 x 6 = 36
7 x 6 = 42
8 x 6 = 48
9 x 6 = 54
10 x 6 = 60
11 x 6 = 66
12 x 6 = 72

10 Times Table

0 x 10 =   0
1 x 10 = 10
2 x 10 = 20
3 x 10 = 30
4 x 10 = 40
5 x 10 = 50
6 x 10 = 60
7 x 10 = 70
8 x 10 = 80
9 x 10 = 90
10 x 10 = 100
11 x 10 = 110
12 x 10 = 120

11 Times Table

0 x 11 =   0
1 x 11 = 11
2 x 11 = 22
3 x 11 = 33
4 x 11 = 44
5 x 11 = 55
6 x 11 = 66
7 x 11 = 77
8 x 11 = 88
9 x 11 = 99
10 x 11 = 110
11 x 11 = 121
12 x 11 = 132

12 Times Table

0 x 12 =   0
1 x 12 = 12
2 x 12 = 24
3 x 12 = 36
4 x 12 = 48
5 x 12 = 60
6 x 12 = 72
7 x 12 = 84
8 x 12 = 96
9 x 12 = 108
10 x 12 = 120
11 x 12 = 132
12 x 12 = 144

Notes

HOMEWORK HELPERS

French

Written by Amanda Doyle
Illustrated by Ian Cunliffe
Educational Consultant: Jo Crocombe

Je me présente

1 un
2 deux
3 trois
4 quatre
5 cinq
6 six
7 sept
8 huit
9 neuf
10 dix

Ma famille

My family

ma grand-mère
My grandmother

mon grand-père
My grandfather

mon frère
My brother

L'heure de la journée

Il est l'heure de se lever.
It's time to get up.

C'est le matin.
It is morning.

Petit déjeuner
Breakfast

Déjeuner
Lunch

C'est l'après-midi.
It is afternoon.

Dîner

Dinner

C'est le soir.

It is evening.

Il est l'heure
de se coucher.

It's time to go to bed.

Le temps

Quel temps fait-il?
What's the weather like?

Il fait beau.
It's fine.

Il pleut.
It's raining.

Il gèle.
It's freezing.

Il neige.
It's snowing.

Il fait chaud.
It's hot.

Il fait froid.
It's cold.

Il y a du vent.
It's windy.

Il fait du soleil.
It's sunny.

Le pique-nique

Dans le sac, il y a...
In the bag there is/are...

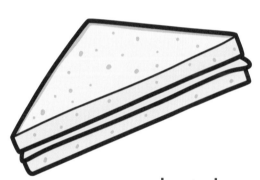

un sandwich
au fromage
a cheese sandwich

une banane
a banana

une pomme
an apple

une orange
an orange

Picnic

des chips
some crisps

de l'eau
some water

des raisins
some grapes

un yaourt
a yoghurt

de la limonade
some lemonade

Le sport

Quel sport fais-tu?
What sport do you do?

Je joue au tennis.
I play tennis.

Je joue au cricket.
I play cricket.

Je joue au basket.
I play basketball.

Sport

Je fais du vélo.
I ride my bike.

Je fais de la danse.
I dance.

Je fais de la natation.
I swim.

Je fais du skate.
I skateboard.

Les animaux

J'ai un lapin.
I have a rabbit.

une araignée
a spider

un chien
a dog

un chat
a cat

un poisson rouge
a goldfish

162

un hamster

a hamster

un serpent

a snake

un lapin

a rabbit

une souris

a mouse

C'est mignon!
It's cute!

En ville

Je cherche
une pâtisserie.
I'm looking for
a cake shop.

une boucherie
a butcher

un café
a cafe

une boulangerie
a bakery

une épicerie
a grocer

In town

un fleuriste
a florist

une pâtisserie
a cake shop

une gare
a railway station

un bureau de poste
a post office

C'est ici!
It's here!

Bon anniversaire!

janvier
January

février
February

mars
March

avril
April

mai
May

juin
June

C'est quand, ton anniversaire? **When is your birthday?**

Mon anniversaire est en janvier! **My birthday is in January!**

Happy birthday!

Je mange des bonbons.
I eat some sweets.

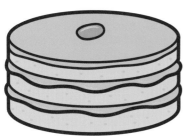

un gâteau
a cake

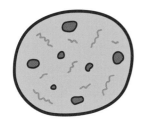

un biscuit
a biscuit

du jus d'orange
some orange juice

J'ai huit ans!
I am eight years old!

juillet
July

août
August

septembre
September

octobre
October

novembre
November

décembre
December

Au concert

J'entends un violon.
I hear a violin.

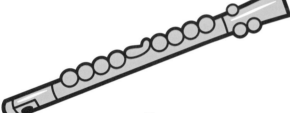

une flûte
a flute

une guitare
a guitar

une flûte à bec
a recorder

un piano
a piano

At the concert

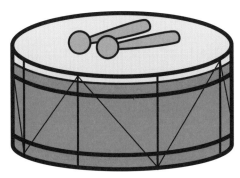

un tambour
a drum

une trompette
a trumpet

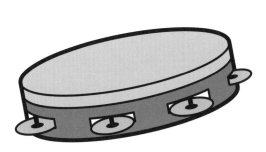

un tambourin
a tambourine

un violon
a violin

Incroyable!
Unbelievable!

Mes vêtements

Je porte
un pull bleu.
**I'm wearing
a blue jumper.**

un chapeau noir
a black hat

une jupe orange
an orange skirt

une casquette rouge
a red cap

une chemise jaune
a yellow shirt

My clothes

une écharpe rose
a pink scarf

un pull bleu
a blue jumper

un pantalon vert
a pair of green trousers

un T-shirt blanc
a white T-shirt

Très chic!
Very smart!

rouge

orange

jaune

vert

bleu

noir

blanc

rose

Au restaurant

Menu

 un sandwich au jambon
a ham sandwich

 du pain
some bread

 un gâteau
a cake

 une limonade
a lemonade

 un chocolat chaud
a hot chocolate

Bon appétit!
Enjoy!

Informations supplémentaires

Les jours de la semaine
The days of the week

lundi	**Monday**
mardi	**Tuesday**
mercredi	**Wednesday**
jeudi	**Thursday**
vendredi	**Friday**
samedi	**Saturday**
dimanche	**Sunday**

Les mois de l'année
The months of the year

janvier	**January**	juillet	**July**
février	**February**	août	**August**
mars	**March**	septembre	**September**
avril	**April**	octobre	**October**
mai	**May**	novembre	**November**
juin	**June**	décembre	**December**

Les nombres
Numbers

10	dix
20	vingt
30	trente
40	quarante
50	cinquante
60	soixante
70	soixante-dix
80	quatre-vingt
90	quatre-vingt-dix
100	cent

Conversation
Conversation

Bonjour!	Hello!
Salut!	Hi!
Au revoir	Goodbye
Comment ça va?	How are you?
Je m'appelle	My name is
J'ai huit ans	I am eight years old
J'habite	I live

Spelling Answers

Pages 4–5
Let's get started!
cap
drum
clock
spider

Happy endings
boat
umbrella
crab
shell
octopus
starfish

Pages 6–7
Jungle japes
g l q w

Short and sweet
cat
bed
pin
fox
sun
peg

A little longer
bee
flute
kite

Pages 8–9
Lots of plurals
apples
cups
boxes
dresses
torches
dishes

Farm count-up
horses
fish
sheep
cows
children
mice

Pages 10–11
Delightful describing
dirty hairy smelly
muddy spotty
stony slimy rosy
stripy nosy icy shiny

Weather watch
rainy
windy
cloudy
snowy
sunny
frosty
stormy

Pages 14–15
Right here, right now
playing
jumping
kicking
reading
walking
looking

sitting digging

caring moving making

A trip to the circus
The girl is clapping her hands.

The strongman is lifting weights.

This clown is riding on his unicycle.

This clown is juggling balls.

Pages 16–17
Done and dusted
pushed pulled

jogged hopped

raced smiled hoped

Rowdy rulebreakers!
Greetings, me hearties! One sunset I **saw** another ship pass in the distance. I gave the order to raise the mainsail. The wind **blew** us there in no time. As soon as we got close by, my men **ran** to grab their weapons. They could tell that the ship belonged to pirates, like us!

I **sat** downstairs in my cabin, trying to come up with a plan. Just then there was a knock on the door. My cabin boy explained that the strange ship belonged to my brother, Old Jack Barnacles!

That night we **ate**
a grand feast, both
crews singing until the
early hours.
The funniest thing about
our jolly evening? My
lazy parrot, George,
slept through the
whole party!
One-Eyed Toby

Pages 18–19
What is the opposite?
tidy untidy
displease
disappear
disobey

All change!
It was time for the
children to get
undressed, ready for PE.

Gemma untied her
shoelaces and pulled off
her hat.

Sarah unzipped her
jacket and hung it on
a hook.

Thomas disliked the
green T-shirt he had
to wear.

Pages 20–21
Sounds like...
flower   flour
blue   blew
son   sun
leak   leek

Jolly jokes
Why can't a car play
football?
It's only got one boot.

Why did the teacher
wear sunglasses?
His pupils were too
bright.

Why did the cat jump
out of the tree?
Because it saw the
tree bark.

What do you get if you
cross a sheep with a
kangaroo?
A woolly jumper.

Pages 22–23
Shh! Letters in hiding
knife   witch
whale   wreck

Funny photos!
lamb
walking
writing
gnome

Pages 24–25
Two for the price of one
sunflower
seahorse
handbag
starfish

Find the compounds
sunshine
upstairs
bathroom
bedroom
wallpaper
downstairs

Pages 28–29
*Keep your eye on
the ball*
kick
hit

Homophone fill-in
She blew up the blue
balloon.

I have a sore eye.

He can see the sea.

Land ahoy!
pirate
hat
tree
ship
island
waves

Adding Up Answers

Pages 62-63
Count the candles
5 candles
2 candles
7 candles

10 candles
There are 14 children at
your party.

Fun with one
8 party hats
3 sandwiches
4 balls
6 jellies

Pages 64-65
Two for tea
9 strawberries
5 onions
4 loaves
8 oranges

Plus 2 practice
$2 + 7 = 9$
$6 + 2 = 8$
$8 + 2 = 10$

Some more sums
$9 + 2 = 11$
$4 + 2 = 6$
$2 + 5 = 7$

Zero zone
$1 + 0 = 1$
$4 + 0 = 4$
$6 + 0 = 6$

Pages 66-67
Ten pin teaser
$3 + 5 = 8$
$4 + 2 = 6$
$2 + 5 = 7$
$8 + 1 = 9$

The girl needs to knock down
5 pins with her second throw
to score a perfect 10.

Spot the spots
$4 + 5 = 9$
$3 + 5 = 8$
$6 + 6 = 12$
$2 + 3 = 5$
$5 + 6 = 11$

Pages 68-69
Animal antics
$2 + 3 = 5$ mice
$5 + 4 = 9$ giraffes
$4 + 8 = 12$ spiders
$6 + 4 = 10$ seagulls
$3 + 2 = 5$ animals

Nibbling numbers
number 9 fish
number 15 fish
number 11 fish

Pages 70-71
Up and down the line
$16 + 5 = 21$
$8 + 8 = 16$
$14 + 5 = 19$
$3 + 9 = 12$
$4 + 4 = 8$
$13 + 7 = 20$

Train-track maths
$9 + 4 = 13$
$10 + 8 = 18$
$2 + 13 = 15$
$15 + 4 = 19$

Pages 72-73
Perfect pairs
$4 + 6 = 10$
$7 + 3 = 10$
$6 + 4 = 10$
$5 + 5 = 10$

Pages 74-75
Top toys
$20 + 7 + 3 = 30$
$6 + 3 + 3 = 12$
$2 + 3 + 4 = 9$

Jungle hide and seek
$5 + 10 + 12 = 27$
$7 + 7 + 7 + 8 = 29$
$1 + 3 + 4 + 1 = 9$
$9 + 11 + 3 = 23$
$10 + 13 + 17 = 40$
$3 + 4 + 2 + 6 = 15$

Pages 76-77
Cloud cover
$15 + 25 = 40$
$10 + 9 = 19$
$8 + 4 = 12$
$4 + 25 = 29$
$14 + 22 = 36$
$13 + 13 = 26$

Daft doublers
$6 + 6 = 12$
$7 + 7 = 14$

Pages 78-79
Message in a bottle
53 days
24 days
3 ships
15 animals

Pages 80-81
Market day
26 HORSES $12 + 14 = 26$
38 GEESE $16 + 22 = 38$
55 CHICKENS $22 + 33 = 55$
47 COWS $6 + 41 = 47$
25 PIGS $11 + 14 = 25$

Counting sheep
$12 + 19 = 31$ lambs
$28 + 14 = 42$ ewes
$15 + 27 = 42$ rams

Pages 82-83
Plus is no fuss
$35 + 7 = 42$
$26 + 24 = 50$
$19 + 17 = 36$
$34 + 12 = 46$

Number grids
There are several right answers. Ask a friend or a grown-up to check yours!

Pages 84-85
Food festival!
apple 10p + 5p
pizza 50p + 5p
juice 10p + 5p + 2p + 1p
spaghetti £1 + £1 + 20p + 20p + 5p
potato 50p + 20p + 2p + 2p

Pages 88-89
Chocolate challenge
15 + 4 = 19 chunks
of chocolate
12 + 4 = 16 chunks
of chocolate
16 + 15 = 31 chunks
of chocolate

Pirate problems
10 sails
12 cannons
18 gold coins

Eight is great
14 + 74 = 88
26 + 62 = 88
45 + 43 = 88
77 + 11 = 88
53 + 35 = 88
69 + 19 = 88
39 + 49 = 88
87 + 1 = 88

Counting crossword
Clues across:
1. 1 + 1 + 3 = 5   f i v e
2. 9 + 2 + 5 = 16   s i x t e e n
3. 2 + 5 + 3 = 10   t e n
4. 4 + 4 + 1 = 9   n i n e

Clues down:
1. 2 + 1 + 1 = 4   f o u r
2. 3 + 4 + 1 = 8   e i g h t
3. 7 + 1 + 3 = 11   e l e v e n
4. 2 + 2 + 3 = 7   s e v e n
5. 5 + 4 + 3 = 12   t w e l v e

Taking Away Answers

Pages 92-93
Cuckoo counting
12 11 10 9 8 7 6 5 4 3 2
1 0

Fee-fi-fo one!
4 cookies and 1 less is 3.
2 apples and 1 less is 1.
5 bunches of cherries and 1 less is 4.
3 sandwiches and 1 less is 2.
9 sweets and 1 less is 8.

Pages 94-95
Up, up and away
5 ducks take away 2 leaves 3.
9 kites take away 2 leaves 7.
4 balloons take away 2 leaves 2.
6 butterflies take away 2 leaves 4.

Royal washing
8 − 0 = 8
3 − 0 = 3
6 − 0 = 6

Rainy runaways
3 − 1 = 2
9 − 2 = 7
7 − 3 = 4
2 − 1 = 1
4 − 2 = 2
5 − 2 = 3

Pages 96-97
Subtraction spells
6 socks minus 3 socks = 3
10 spiders minus 5 spiders = 5
4 bats minus 2 bats = 2

Fairytale fun
Take away 4
3 8 1 6 4 0

Take away 3
9 3 6 8 5 1 4

Take away 6
2 4 1 6 8 3 5

Nursery numbers
13 − 3 = 10

14 − 4 = 10

14 − 6 = 8
10 − 2 = 8

14 − 12 = 2
9 − 7 = 2

11 − 4 = 7
8 − 1 = 7

12 − 6 = 6
15 − 9 = 6

Pages 98-99
Domino difference
The difference is 3.
The difference is 3.
The difference is 0.

Dotty dice
The total of (3 + 6 + 5 = 14) minus
(3 + 1 + 2 = 6) is 8.   14 − 6 = 8

The total of (4 + 6 + 2 = 12) minus
(2 + 4 + 6 = 12) is 0.
12 − 12 = 0

Ball games
The difference between 9 marbles and 3 marbles is 6.

4 footballs is 4 less than 8 footballs.

Counting back 3 beach balls from 12 beach balls takes us to 9.

10 tennis balls take away 8 tennis balls equals 2.

Take 2 juggling balls from 3 balls to leave 1.

6 barbells subtract 2 equals 4.

Pages 100-101
Hop to the spot
22 − 7 = 15

18 − 6 = 12
12 − 9 = 3
25 − 5 = 20

Bigger jumps backwards
18 − 14 = 4
12 − 10 = 2
25 − 19 = 6
38 − 23 = 15
49 − 21 = 28

Pages 102-103
All change
2p change
5p change
8p change
6p change
1p change

Twenty pence price challenge
Cap – change 10p coin and a 5p coin
Trousers – change 2p coin
Shirt – change 2p coin and a 1p coin
Scarf – change 5p coin and a 2p coin
Jumper – change 5p coin
T shirt – change 10p coin

No. The boy does not have enough for the blue jumper.

Yes. The girl could afford to buy the red cap as well as the pink scarf.

Pages 104-105
Hungry pups
FIFI – 16
SPOT – 21
SCRUFFY – 8
BRUISER – 13

The right and the wrong way
8 − 5 = 3 √   5 − 8 = 3 X

Purr-fect opposites
23 − 8 = 15
15 + 8 = 23

$18 - 7 = 11$
$11 + 7 = 18$

$29 - 16 = 13$
$13 + 16 = 29$

$24 - 5 = 19$
$19 + 5 = 24$

Pages 106-107
Daring diving
$46 - 35 = 11$
$17 - 8 = 9$
$41 - 5 = 36$
$34 - 18 = 16$
$29 - 14 = 15$

Jiggly jellyfish
3 jellyfish have 24 tentacles.
Half of 24 is 12.
2 jellyfish have 16 tentacles.
Half of 16 is 8.
4 jellyfish have 32 tentacles.
Half of 32 is 16.

Pages 108-109
A visit from Vanessa

50 children are in the show.
The difference is 45p.
The gloves were 15p more.
There will be 5 buses running.

Kai's sticker sums
15 people are in the photo.
The difference is 14.
Kai sold 8 more things on
Sunday.
Kai's dad saved 4 kilometres.

Pages 110-111
Big game test
$81 - 58 = 23$ √
$56 - 47 = 13$ X
$70 - 44 = 26$ √
$56 - 44 = 12$ √
$99 - 33 = 54$ X
$28 - 17 = 11$ √
$45 - 16 = 28$ X
$39 - 21 = 19$ X
$44 - 12 = 32$ √

Bird brain-teasers
$51 - 38 = 13$

$72 - 25 = 47$

$93 - 56 = 37$

Page 112
Learning ladders
Numbers for the first ladder:
73
$- 9$
64
$- 20$
44
$- 6$
38

Numbers for the second ladder:
49
$- 18$
31
$- 5$
26
$- 12$
$= 14$

Numbers for the third ladder:
52
$- 31$
21
$- 8$
13
$- 8$
$= 5$

Numbers for the fourth ladder:
68
$- 23$
45
$- 17$
28
$- 26$
$= 2$

Page 113
Crazy code breaker
Key:-
A – 8
B – 13
C – 21
D – 4
E – 18
F – 25
G – 24
H – 9
I – 2
J – 11
K – 20
L – 6
M – 26
N – 16
O – 14
P – 1
Q – 12
R – 3

S – 15
T – 22
U – 17
V – 5
W – 23
X – 10
Y – 7
Z – 19

The message is...
I COULD TAKE AWAY ALL
DAY!

Pages 114-115
Find a flight
Glasgow and Edinburgh
£42
£62
Manchester and London
£7
ONE TICKET TO EXETER

Holiday shopping
A 50p coin and a 5p coin
Two £1 coins
Four £1 coins and a 1p coin
Three £1 coins, a 50p coin
and a 20p.

Pages 118-119
Split the difference
2 sheep on the left and 9 on the
right. The difference is 7.

11 pigs on the left and 6 on the
right. The difference is 5.

Subtraction action
$88 - 63 = 25$
$64 - 24 = 40$
$96 - 45 = 51$
$19 - 13 = 6$

Take away 9
58 29 76 83 19 65 22 36 39

Take away 18
30 21 2 39 79 66 16 1 54

Notes

Notes

Notes